Preface

This maintenance textbook has been prepared by Parker Hannifin to provide the user of industrial hydraulic equipment a detailed reference in the areas of maintenance and troubleshooting.

The textbook has been arranged to begin with a discussion of the basic principles of maintenance and troubleshooting. Over the years, it has been realized that many maintenance people have considered the technique of "parts changing" as an effective way of solving problems within a hydraulic system.

One very important area of maintenance that we have tried to address is graphic symbology. Although the maintenance personnel, in general, are not responsible for the drawing of hydraulic equipment schematics, oftentimes the understanding of graphic symbols that represent the hydraulic components in a system is the only key to diagnosing a problem. Because of the complexity of modern hydraulic systems, your ability to read a schematic will be an invaluable asset in troubleshooting.

As you review each section of this textbook, you'll find at the end of the section, troubleshooting charts that list common problems, causes of the problem, and possible remedies of the problem. These charts can serve as excellent references to have in your tool box.

We would like to thank all the people who contributed to the writing and organization of the material contained in this textbook. We sincerely hope that you, the reader, will find this material valuable and useful and we invite your constructive criticism.

Table of Contents

HYDRAULIC MAINTENANCE INTRODUCTION

Hydraulic Maintenance

There are many people that think hydraulic maintenance (troubleshooting) is an art rather than systematic progression of checks and evaluations.

There are actually two ways to approach the area of troubleshooting. The first and most frequently used method is that of "Hit-or-Miss". This method utilizes the age old practice of changing parts or readjusting valve settings in the hydraulic system until the problem is solved. This is not only time consuming, but costly from the standpoint of parts, labor cost and equipment down time. Too many times we only correct a symptom to a problem and don't really solve the problem. We, at best, have established a temporary fix.

The other, more efficient method is to start out using your brain. Get all the facts, examine them, draw conclusions and finally test these conclusions until the problem is discovered. In short, think through the problem, i.e. analyze the cause, examine the symptoms, formulate a solution, implement it and review the results.

Typical Hydraulic Circuit Schematic

Every hydraulic circuit follows a logical sequence of operations determined by the type of components within the circuit and how they are interconnected.

When a circuit will not operate properly, there is a logical reason for the malfunction. Step-by-step diagnosis and testing of the circuit will lead you to the problem in the shortest possible time.

Principles of Diagnosis and Testing

Most troubleshooting occurs in either "start-up" or "breakdown" situations. Each case will pro-

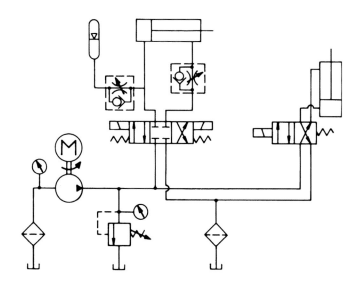

vide its own set of clues and require slightly different techniques on the part of the troubleshooter.

Regardless of which situation exists, certain general diagnosis and testing steps will always apply:

1. Take nothing for granted. Satisfy yourself as to whether a safe condition exists.

2. Keep your hands in your pockets, stop to think before you act, take your time, talk to the operator and obtain as much information as possible.

3. Know the system, get a controls drawing, a power diagram, operation- al sequence, etc.

4. Visually inspect the machine.

5. Operate the machine.

6. Check all services to the machine, electrical, high pressure steam, gas lines, or any power devices you do not control, such as accumulators.

7. Isolate legs of the circuit. Avoid open lines.

8. Identify the problem such as:

   • No actuator movement

   • Slow or erratic actuator movement

   • Noise and vibration

   • Heat

9. Match the problem to the cause:

   • Low pressure

   • Low flow

   • Erratic component operation

10. Reach a conclusion.

11. Test your conclusion.

12. Report your findings.

13. Repair and/or replace components as necessary

Let's see what each step means.

Take Nothing for Granted

Satisfy yourself as to whether safe conditions exist. Don't take the word of someone else regarding a critical item, such as determining if there is any electrical power turned on. He may not know what he is talking about. You could get electrocuted, so you check it out.

Keep Your Hands in Your Pocket

Resist the temptation to "dive" in. Resist any pressures such as "Don't just stand there! Do something!" until you are certain of what the results of your actions will be.

Stop to think before you act, this is probably the most important step, and the one most often overlooked. A serviceman's easiest form of diagnosis is to stop for a moment and talk to the person who is most familiar with the operation of the machine, the operator.

Try to find out if this problem has occurred before and if so, when, who did the servicing, and what was done to correct the problem. Often machine records will be a valuable source of diagnosis information. If no records have been kept, then you must begin your diagnosis by visually inspecting the machine.

Know the System

Every machine has or has had some type of hydraulic circuit schematic and/or technical manual that will explain the operation of the machine. You should find out if this type of information exists.

Check to see if there is an accumulator in the system. Make sure it is discharged before disconnecting any hydraulic lines.

You must familiarize yourself with the machine such as, is it an open-loop or closed-loop system, what is the recommended system pressure, what type of pump(s), valve(s), accumulator(s) and actuators are there in the system and what are their individual outputs, what is the sequence of operation, etc.

Many manufacturers publish service bulletins that will keep you up-to-date on the latest developments in their machines. That problem that you are currently trying to solve may be in one of the bulletins, with information as to the cause and the remedy.

Visually Inspect the Machine

Visually inspect the machine to familiarize yourself with its mechanisms and general layout. Ask as many pertinent questions as you can from anyone present who is in a position to inform you.

Operate the Machine

After discussing the problem with the operator, operate the machine yourself, to see if the problem occurs for you as it did with the operator.

Get the machine up to operating temperature. Some things you'll be looking for:

- Does the system pressure match the specifications found on the schematic?

- On manually operated controls are--they hard or sloppy?

- Do you smell any unusual odors?

- Do you see any external leaks at the rod glands, valve ports, etc?

Check All Services to the Machine

Before attempting to service the machine after you have operated it, check to see if there is electricity on the machine. Are there any high pressure steam lines, gas lines or any power devices which you do not control? Check to make sure that if an accumulator(s) is installed on the machine that it is fully discharged of fluid before disconnecting any hydraulic lines.

Isolate Legs of the Circuit--Avoid Open Lines

Many times a problem occurs because of a malfunction in another leg of the system. This can be hard to find if the various legs are not isolated.

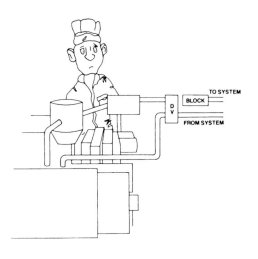

As an example: "Slow actuator movement." This type of problem should immediately bring to mind the relationship between actuator speed and flow. Therefore, look for the lost flow. One possible cause of this could be low pump volume into the system. The output of the pump should be checked at rated rpm and pressure.

NOTE: As a safety precaution, any lines or ports that are disconnected should be capped to prevent unnecessary oil leakage while the machine is operating as well as the ingestion of dirt into open lines by using the proper hex plug or cap or flange plate.

While operating the machine, keep close watch on system pressure; be careful not to exceed maximum system pressure.

Identify the Problem

In your inspection of the machine the problem may be quite obvious. However, there may be some hidden causes that must be identified.

As an example: "No actuator movement" could be caused by a malfunctioning pump, low or no oil, or stuck actuator.

Make a list of possible causes. What were the things you found when you operated the machine? What is the most likely cause of the problem? One thing that should be kept in mind is that one failure could be the result of another failure elsewhere in the system.

Match the Problem to the Cause

Principles of component and system operation must be thoroughly understood in order for you to diagnose the problem accurately.

When the ability to move a load is hampered, you have to understand that it is the effects of pressure acting on some area that develops force or torque. And it is the amount of flow entering an actuator that determines the speed of the actuator.

By understanding these and other basic principles you will save time in reaching a conclusion about what the cause of the problem is.

Reach a Conclusion

Refer back to your list of possible causes and decide which ones are most likely to relate to the problem and which ones are the easiest to test first.

Test your Conclusion

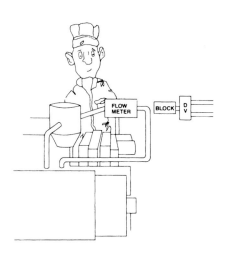

Testing your conclusion can be as simple as checking the oil level in the reservoir, but you must analyze the information you've gathered. By testing, instead of replacing parts, you begin to eliminate possible causes until the exact cause is pinpointed.

After the failure or malfunction has been determined your findings should be reported to those people who will decide on the action to take.

Report Your Findings

Reporting your findings not only means talking to those people who make the final decision as to whether a component should be repaired or replaced, it also means making notes on the schematic as to what components were removed from and/or added to the machine's circuitry.

NOTE: This portion of step 9 will require a good understanding of hydraulic symbology.

Another worthwhile practice to begin is to create a machine file. In this file place all information gathered about this machine; it also serves as a reference should any future reccurring or new problems happen.

Repair and/or Replace Components as Necessary

Component repair and/or replacement is the final step in the step-by-step progression of diagnosis and troubleshooting.

One last consideration that has a major impact on reducing downtime is preventive maintenance. Simply repairing or replacing a component alone is only a stop gap measure if steps are not taken to prevent reccurrence of the same failure. A good preventive maintenance program is an essential part of any service departments function.

Review

By consistently following these steps as shown, maintenance personnel can become effective troubleshooters rather than "Hit-or-Miss" hammer mechanics.

1. Take nothing for granted.

2. Keep your hands in your pockets.

3. Know the system.

4. Visually inspect the machine.

5. Operate the machine.

6. Check all services to the machine. Check for accumulator(s) on the machine.

7. Isolate legs of the circuit.

8. Identify the problem.

9. Match the problem to the cause.

10. Reach a conclusion.

11. Test your conclusion.

12. Report your findings.

13. Repair and/or replace.

HYDRAULIC GRAPHIC SYMBOLOGY

One of the first steps in diagnosis and testing is to get a schematic of the hydraulic, electric and any other system on the machine to be analyzed. The schematic is the "road map" to the hydraulic system. What if no schematic exists? One line of thought to remedy this problem is for you to draw the schematic or at least have someone do this. If you draw the schematic, it will help you better understand the system and greatly simplify your troubleshooting. Therefore, a thorough understanding of the graphic symbols for fluid power systems and components is necessary.

ANSI (American National Standards Institute) and ISO (International Organization for Standardization) are the two recognized standards bodies for fluid power system and component graphic symbols.

Many companies create their own symbols for their components; however, this practice should be discontinued and avoided because of the confusion it can and does cause.

The ISO symbols have become the standard for international usage; therefore, we'll look at these symbols in greater detail. There are six categories that comprise all of the symbols. It is the intent of this section to thoroughly acquaint you with these symbols and then utilize them in developing simple systems as well as diagnose problems using some actual system schematics.

"Graphic symbols shown in accordance with ISO 1219, Fluid Power Systems and Components - Graphic Symbols."

When this phrase is seen on test reports, schematics, catalogs and sales literature it means that all symbols used comply to the ISO Standard, ISO 1219-1976.

General Symbols

The symbols commonly used in drawing hydraulic equipment and any accessory equipment are either pictorial, cutaway or graphic symbols. There is no prescribed layout or scale size for the symbols.

Generally in drawing a circuit diagram, the draftsperson will represent the equipment in the non-actuated (at rest) condition. This does not preclude other conditions from being represented, but it should be clearly stated that some other condition exists when such a situation occurs.

Pictorial symbols are very useful for showing the interconnection of components. They are not standardized from a functional basis. Cutaway symbols emphasize construction. These symbols are complex to draw and the functions are not readily apparent.

Graphic symbols emphasize the function and methods of operation of components. These symbols are simple to draw. Graphic symbols are capable of crossing language barriers, and can promote a universal understanding of fluid power systems.

When the draftsperson draws the diagram, they have the choice of using either complete graphic symbols, simplified graphic symbols, or composite graphic symbols.

Complete graphic symbols are those which give symbolic representation of the component and all of its features pertinent to the circuit diagram.

Simplified graphic symbols are stylized versions of the complete symbols.

Composite graphic symbols are an organization of simplified or complete symbols. Composite symbols usually represent a complex component.

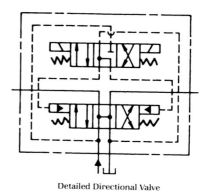

Detailed Directional Valve

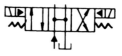

Simplified Directional Valve

General Characteristics of Symbols

All graphic symbols will take on one of the basic elementary forms, such as:

- Circles
- Rectangles
- Arcs
- Dots
- Squares
- Triangles
- Arrows
- Crosses
- Lines - Solid or dashed

When drawing these symbols, there are some clear rules to follow in order to make the graphic symbols recognizable on the international level.

1. Symbols show connections, flow paths, and functions of components represented.

2. They can indicate conditions occurring during transition from one flow path arrangement to another.

3. Symbols do not indicate construction, nor do they indicate values, such as pressure, flow rate, and other component settings.

4. Symbols do not indicate the location of actual valve ports, direction of shifting of spools, or the actual mounting of actuators in machines.

5. Symbols may be rotated or reversed without altering their meaning except in cases of lines to reservoirs, vented manifolds and accumulators.

6. The means of operating fluid power components are shown as part of the symbol (where applicable).

7. Symbols using words or their abbreviations are avoided.

8. Simplified symbols are shown for commonly used components.

Lines

The basic symbols of lines consists of continuous lines for main flow lines; long dashes for pilot pressure lines; short dashes for drain lines.

Lines that are connected by tees and crosses are denoted by a dot at the point of intersection. Lines that cross over one another but do not intersect, can be denoted by not putting a dot at the crossover point or by putting a loop in one line.

Double lines are mechanical connections such as motor shafts, hand levers and cylinder rods. Several components that are assembled as a complete unit are represented by a series of long and short lines that enclose them.

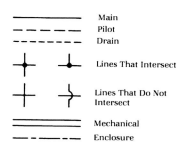

Circles, Semi-Circles, Squares, Rectangles and Diamonds

The basic symbol of a circle or semi-circle represents energy conversion components such as a pump and/or motor. Smaller diameter circles are used as measuring instruments (pressure and vacuum gauges), non-return valve, rotary connection, mechanical links and rollers.

The square and rectangle are generally reserved for control valves except for non-return type valves. The single square can also be used to represent an internal combustion engine. Therefore, the basic symbol can be used to represent several different components.

Commonly known as envelopes, the squares joined in series will tell you how many distinct operating positions a valve may assume such as two, three or four. When there are three positions

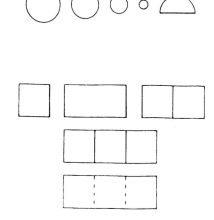

indicated, but they are separated by dash lines, it means that the valve is being used as a two position valve with some type of crossover center condition.

Filtration, cooling and heating of fluids will use the basic symbol of the diamond to represent the conditioning apparatus.

Miscellaneous Symbols

Other basic symbols would include flow line connections, springs and flow restrictions, which are orifices in the flow path; one that is affected by fluid viscosity changes and the other is unaffected by viscosity changes. The triangle is considered a functional symbol that represents the direction of flow of the fluid and the nature of the fluid whether liquid or gaseous.

Arrows indicate direction, direction or rotation, and, path and direction of flow through a valve.

In the path and direction of flow, arrows note the perpendicular line to the arrow head. This indicates as a general rule that when the arrow moves, the interior path always remains connected to the corresponding exterior path as will be shown in pressure control valves.

A sloping arrow, generally a 45° slope, indicates the ability to vary or regulate in a progressive manner.

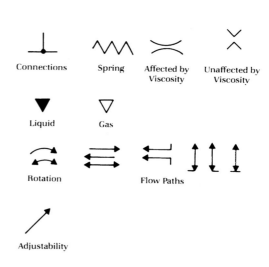

Energy Conversion Components

The next category represents the components that convert energy. Pumps convert mechanical energy into hydraulic energy; motors, cylinders and rotary actuators convert hydraulic energy into mechanical energy.

Pumps

There are two basic types of pumps, fixed and variable displacement capacity. Fixed displacement pumps are represented as shown and can be either unidirectional or bidirectional. The symbol does not, however, tell you whether the pump is a vane, piston or gear pump.

Two-stage or double pumps are represented by two individual unidirectional pump symbols joined together with a mechanical connection symbol (double horizontal lines).

Variable volume displacement and pressure compensated pumps are also unidirectional and bidirectional. The sloping arrow through the pump represents variable volume and the square with the arrow inside represents pressure compensation.

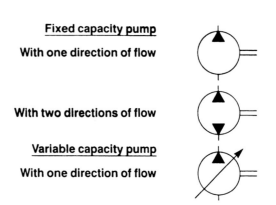

Fixed capacity pump

With one direction of flow

With two directions of flow

Variable capacity pump

With one direction of flow

When the pump symbol is drawn, note the two small external lines that are in series with the arrowhead(s). These are the inlet and outlet of the pump.

Arrowhead(s) inside the circle shall be solid and point outward to indicate hydraulic fluid flow is directed outward, into the circuit. All pumps are driven by a prime mover that would be coupled to the pump using the mechanical connection symbol (double horizontal lines).

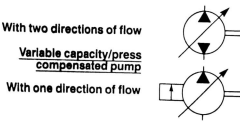

With two directions of flow

Variable capacity/press compensated pump

With one direction of flow

Motors

Motor symbols are quite similar to the pump symbols for fixed and variable displacement as well as unidirectional and bidirectional rotation. The major difference is in the position of the internal arrowhead(s). Note the arrowhead is solid, but points inward to indicate fluid is directed into the component.

The semi-circle, called an oscillating motor, is representative of a rotary actuator. This symbol, like the other motor symbols, does not indicate the type of motor being used.

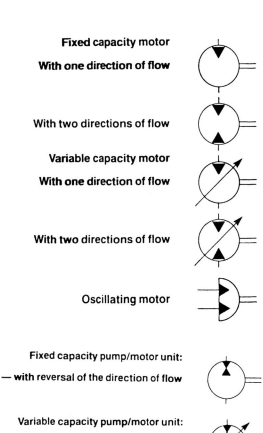

Fixed capacity motor

With one direction of flow

With two directions of flow

Variable capacity motor

With one direction of flow

With two directions of flow

Oscillating motor

Pump-Motor Units

A more specialized motor is the pump/motor unit with two functions. It either operates as a pump or as a rotary motor. There are fixed volume pump/motors that can reverse the direction of flow, have single flow direction or be bidirectional in flow. The variable volume pump/motors are similar with the addition of a sloping arrow to indicate the volume may be changed.

Fixed capacity pump/motor unit:
— **with reversal of the direction of flow**

Variable capacity pump/motor unit:
— **with reversal of the direction of flow**

Cylinders

Cylinders are used to convert hydraulic energy into mechanical force by the application of fluid pressure to the surface area of the piston.

Single Acting Cylinders

The simplest type of cylinder is the single acting cylinder in which the fluid pressure acts on one side of the piston and in one direction. Usually in the forward stroke. The symbol for a cylinder that needs an external force will have the rod end of the cylinder opened to indicate it is open to atmosphere. At the base end is a small vertical line to indicate the port where fluid enters and leaves the cylinder. There is also the single acting spring returned cylinder. In the example, fluid pressure will stroke the cylinder forward while spring force will retract the cylinder.

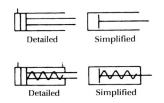

Detailed   Simplified

Detailed   Simplified

Double Acting Cylinders

Double acting cylinders are either single or double rod type. The small vertical lines at each end represents the ports where fluid enters and leaves the cylinder.

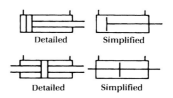

Detailed   Simplified

Detailed   Simplified

Differential Cylinders and Cylinders with Cushions

Differential cylinders better known as 2:1 cylinders are denoted by the large rod size in the symbol. This is also a double acting cylinder as represented by the two small vertical lines (ports).

Cylinders that are equipped with cushion assemblies at either or both ends of the cylinder are represented as shown. The cushion symbol does not indicate the cushion type. That is, straight, tapered, stepped, etc., but it will indicate whether it is fixed or adjustable.

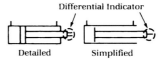

Differential Indicator

Detailed   Simplified

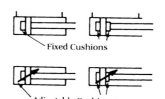

Fixed Cushions

Adjustable Cushions

Telescopic Cylinders

When cylinders contain more than one rod and these rods collapse inside one another, it is called a telescoping cylinder. They can be either single acting or double acting.

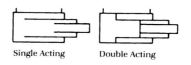

Single Acting   Double Acting

Pressure Intensifier

A specialized cylinder containing two pistons of different areas, connected with a common rod is known as a pressure intensifier. The intensifier can have similar fluids entering and leaving the ports as shown by the open triangles at each end of the symbol. There is also a center port indicated by the small vertical line that is a bleed-to-atmosphere port.

When dissimilar fluids (e.g. air and oil) are used as indicated by the open and darkened triangles, the cylinder body is divided into two parts. To the left, air pressure enters and there is a small vertical line representing an air-bleed. In the right half, hydraulic fluid exits and a drain line is shown on the bottom.

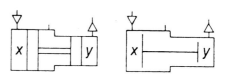

for one type of fluid

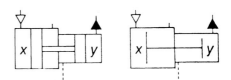

for two types of fluid

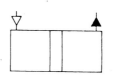

Air-oil actuator

Control Valves

In control valve symbology, the square is used for housing valve functions such as controlling flow, direction of flow and/or pressure. The single square indicates a component used for controlling flow or pressure, various conditions may exist inside with regard to the operating condition of the component.

2-6

Two or more squares together indicate a directional control valve having as many positions as there are squares. The external piping as represented by the small vertical lines are normally connected to the square representing the inoperative or non-actuated condition. The operating positions are determined by imagining the squares moving right or left until the ports of the various conditions represented inside the squares, line up with the external piping.

Many times in a schematic, the same type valve can be used several times. To save time in drawing the symbol repeatedly, a simplified symbol for the valve is used. The number inside the square refers to a note on the schematic in which the symbol for the valve is drawn in detail.

NOTE: Though this practice is used, in very complex diagrams, it can be very time consuming and confusing having to refer to the referenced valve each time you encounter this symbol.

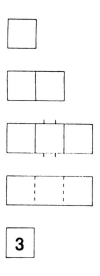

Flow Paths

Various flow paths may exist in one directional valve symbol. The most common types are:

- One flow path, the arrowhead shows direction of flow and it can be drawn in either direction.

- Two closed ports, represented by two "T's" in the square, indicates no flow between the ports.

- Two flow paths in a single square indicates a four ported valve with flow in two directions.

- Two flow paths in a single square with cross connection indicates that all four ports are connected.

- One flow path in a bypass condition and two closed ports, indicate that the flow, e.g. from the pump enters the valve and exits the valve back to tank while the other ports are blocked.

The number of ports in a valve, which allows flow through them or blocks flow at the port indicated in one square are commonly referred to as the number of ways a valve has e.g., 2-way, 3-way or 4-way.

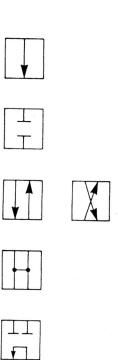

Directional Control Valve Designations 2/2 or 3/2

The 2-way, 2-position, manually controlled valve is often used as a safety or interlock or an on-off function valve. It can be operated in one direction by fluid pressure, manually or electrically and

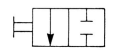

manual control

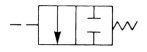

returned to its normal non-actuated position by a spring.

The symbol for a 3-way, 2-position valve is designated by two squares and three ports in each square and this valve is operated by pressure at either end. The other symbol at first glance looks like a 3-position valve controlled by a solenoid and returned by a spring. But notice the center square is separated by dotted lines. This designates the center position as a transitory intermediate condition or crossover condition. Therefore, this too is a 2-position valve.

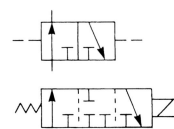

4/2 Directional Valve

A 4-way, 2-position directional valve is designated by two squares each containing four ports. Commonly used to give a reciprocating action to double-acting cylinders or to reverse the rotation of a motor, these valves can be operated directly by either solenoids or fluid pressure. Some are operated by the use of a second 4-way, 2-position valve called a pilot valve. The pilot valve can be operated by two solenoids or a solenoid on one side and a return spring on the other to return the pilot valve to its normally non-actuated position.

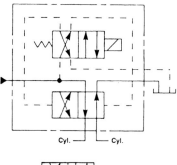

The detail symbol shows an enclosure line around the two valves to indicate that these valves are one unit. The simplified symbol indicates the method of main directional valve controls, e.g. solenoid control, pilot operated, spring offset (return); and the type of main valve section only, a 4-way, 2-position directional control valve.

4/3 Directional Valve

4-way, 3-position directional valves are distinguished by a neutral or intermediate center (at rest) position. This center condition can consist of various flow paths. The four most common are: open center, closed center, tandem center and float center.

These valves are commonly operated by pilot pressure in both directions by means of a second 4-way, 3-position valve called a pilot valve. The center position, for a spring centered, is a float center. Another center position used is a regenerative center for directional valves that have pressure centered main valves.

The pilot valve is controlled by two solenoids and centering springs. The main valve is controlled by pilot pressure and centering springs as shown in the detailed symbol. The simplified symbol shows the main valve positions and the control mechanism. This valve nomenclature is: solenoid controlled, pilot operated, spring centered, 4-way, 3-position directional valve.

Open Center

Closed Center

Tandem Center

Float Center

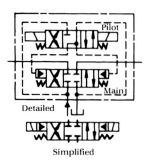

Pilot

Main

Detailed

Simplified

4/3 or 4/4 Mobile Directional Valves

4-way, 3-position or 4-position valves commonly used in mobile hydraulic systems are distinguishable by the open center flow path indicated in the center position.

These valves are commonly operated by levers into the various positions and spring returned to the center position. In some cases an electrical or mechanical device is added to the valve to hold the spool in a desired position. This device is known as a detent.

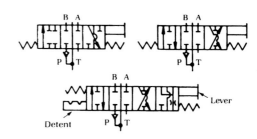

Throttling Directional Control

Throttling directional control valves or proportional valves, have 2 or 3 positions. The center position has an infinite number of intermediate conditions with varying degrees of throttling. Note that all the symbols have parallel lines at top and bottom along the length of the envelopes. These parallel lines indicate an infinite positioning capability, for example: a 2-way, 2-positioned tracer valve with one throttling orifice is shown operated by a plunger against a return spring or a 4-way, 3-position type with four throttling orifices.

Another example of a throttling valve's control is also controlled by pressure against a return spring.

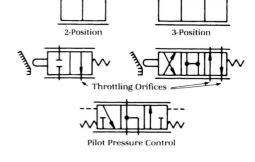

Electrohydraulic Servo Valve

Electrohydraulic servo valves accept an analogue or digital electrical signal and provide a controlled flow (via set spool position) in response to varied current.

There are three basic types: the single stage valve operated electrically (direct), the two stage with mechanical or electrical feedback and pilot pressure operation of the main valve unit; the third type uses hydraulic feedback to indicate valve position and is operated by pilot pressure.

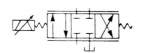

single stage with direct operation

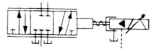

two stage with mechanical feedback with indirect pilot operation

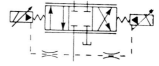

two stage with hydraulic feedback with indirect pilot operation

Non-return Valves Check Valves

Non-return valves are a form of directional control valves. However, they only allow free flow in one direction. Normally known as check valves; there are four common types. A free type check valve contains no spring biasing the moveable member (poppet or ball). It allows flow through it when the incoming pressure is higher than the outlet or back pressure.

Free Check

A spring loaded check is held closed by spring force bias and opens only if inlet pressure is higher than spring pressure plus outlet back pressure.

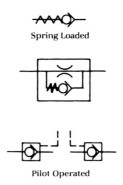
Spring Loaded

Pilot Operated

A common use for this type check valve is shown in conjunction with an orifice symbol. These two symbols are contained in a rectangular box to indicate it is one unit. Pilot operated checks can be either opened by or closed by an external pilot pressure. Often these symbols are drawn incorrectly because people view the arrowhead as indicating direction of free flow. However, the arrowhead represented the seat for the moveable member (ball or poppet). Free flow is in the opposite direction. If any doubt exists, contact the manufacturer.

Shuttle Valves

Another type of directional control valve is a shuttle valve. The ball will move to one side or the other depending on which inlet port has the higher pressure, thus connecting that pressure to the outlet port and blocking the opposite inlet port.

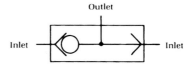

Pressure Control Valves

These symbols in general are represented by a single square with an arrow indicating direction of flow and flow path condition, e.g. normally passing (open) or normally non-passing (closed).

Pressure Relief Valves

Pressure relief or safety valves come in two styles: direct acting fixed or variable and a pilot operated.

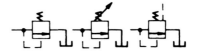

Direct operated reliefs are represented by internal pilot pressure (dotted line) working against a fixed or variable spring pressure. With pilot control, inlet pressure is limited to the combination forces of spring and pilot pressure. These symbols are presented in a normally non-passing (closed) condition. In some diagrams a pilot operated relief valve is represented in a detailed drawing with an orifice between the main valve section and the pilot valve. The two combined symbols are represented inside an enclosure symbol to show that they are contained in one unit.

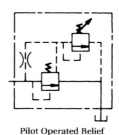
Pilot Operated Relief

Proportional Relief Valve

Another type of pressure relief valve is a proportional relief valve. The inlet pressure is limited by a fixed ratio as determined by the size ratio between the large rectangle and small square.

The valve can be presented in two ways. One is to show internal pilot pressure having to develop a proportionally higher pressure than the remote pilot pressure. The other representation is the reverse action, internal pilot pressure has to be proportionally lower than remote pilot pressure.

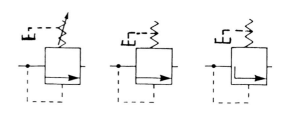

Higher   Lower

Sequence Valve

Sometimes in a system, one operating leg of the system must complete an operation before another operating leg can begin its cycle. This is often controlled by a sequence valve. This valve will remain in its normally non-passing (closed) condition until a specific pressure has been reached in the upstream portion of the system.

Sequence valves require a check valve for reverse flow, can be directly or remotely piloted, and are always externally drained.

Pressure Reducing Valve

In a circuit where one leg may require a lower pressure than the rest of the system, a pressure reducing valve may be installed.

This valve is a normally passing (open) valve as indicated by the interior arrow flow path being aligned with the inlet and outlet ports. The internal pilot is sensing outlet or secondary pressure of the valve. The outlet pressure setting is determined by either spring pressure or external pilot pressure.

This valve is also represented with or without a relief port. This relief port allows secondary pressure that exceeds the pressure setting to be vented back to tank. The double arrowhead interior arrow indicates this flow capability. The perpendicular leg on the interior arrow indicates that the interior flow path always remains connected to the secondary or outlet path and therefore should pressure at the outlet become excessive, the movable member will align with the tank port to relieve.

To achieve reverse flow, a check valve is needed, and this valve requires external draining of the spring cavity.

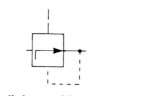

without relief port   **with relief port**

without relief port with remote control

Regulator Valve

These two pressure regulator valves both reduce outlet pressure to a lower pressure than inlet pressure.

A differential pressure valve is represented by a square that has a normally non-passing (closed) interior. As inlet pressure enters the valve, it is moved to a passing position. Pressure in the secondary or outlet port is also directed to the spring side of the valve, thus regulating outlet pressure to a fixed amount determined by the spring valve. This valve can also be represented with an adjustable spring symbol.

A proportional pressure valve is represented by a square that has a normally non-passing interior. The larger rectangle represents the larger control area. The outlet pressure is reduced by a fixed ratio as determined by the size ratio between the large rectangle and the small square.

Flow Control Valves

Flow control valves affect the fluid flow rate. One type is known as a throttle valve. The simplified symbol represents an adjustable restriction commonly called a needle valve. However, a throttle valve detailed symbol shows that the valve can be manually controlled and the state of the valve can be fully non-passing (closed) or fully passing (open).

It can also be mechanically controlled against a return spring. These valves are commonly known as throttling valves. The throttle valves would be affected by variations in the pressure and fluid temperature. There are flow valves that compensate for these variations in pressure and temperature.

Shown are a fixed flow rate, pressure restrictor type; another is fixed flow rate, pressure compensated bypass type with a relief port to reservoir.

The flow rate can also be adjustable as shown with pressure compensation. To show that the valve also compensates for fluid viscosity variation due to temperature, note the different restriction symbol.

Flow Divider Valve

The output flow of a pump can be divided into flows of fixed ratios using a flow divider valve. The resulting flows are substantially independent of one another and of pressure variations in the lines. The symbol shown represents a fixed ration; however, variable outputs can be presented by arrows drawn on a 45° slant through the restriction. This symbol does not differentiate between the types of flow dividers available.

Shut-off Valve

The shut-off valve is primarily used in a closed condition but can also be represented in an open condition by separating the two arrowheads. The symbol can be used to represent a valve or a pipe plug in a valve passage.

Proportional pressure regulator

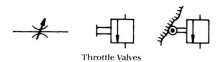

Throttle Valves

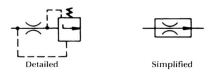

Detailed   Simplified

Fixed Flow Pressure Compensated Restrictor

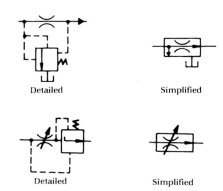

Detailed   Simplified

Adjustable Flow Pressure Compensated Restrictor

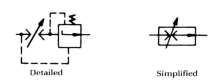

Detailed   Simplified

Adjustable Flow Press.-Temp. Compensated Restrictor

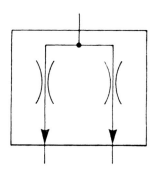

Source of Pressure

Energy transmission and conditioning devices consist of prime movers, pressure sources, flow conduits, energy storage devices, filtration and temperature control devices. When there is some pressure source present in a circuit, a general simplified symbol is used. But when the pressure source must be specified as hydraulic or pneumatic, a closed triangle indicates hydraulics and an open triangle indicates pneumatics.

Prime Movers and Power Take-offs

The prime mover of a hydraulic pump is typically either an electric motor or an internal combustion engine. The two horizontal lines represent a mechanical connection.

In some equipment, such as in mobile applications, a PTO is used and the point where an auxilliary piece of equipment can be connected is represented by a line with an X. The X means that it is plugged, if there is an arrow pointing into the X, the power take-off is connected to some device.

Flow Lines

Long solid continuous lines are the symbols for main working lines, return lines and feedlines; long dashed lines represent pilot control pressure lines; short dashed lines represent drains or bleed lines.

A line that is flexible, such as a rubber hose, that connects two moving parts is represented by a concave line with dots at each end. The dots are points of connection. Sometimes electrical lines are drawn in a hydraulic circuit diagram and they are represented as a solid line with an electrical symbol pointing to the line.

Lines that are connected, such as with tees or crosses, are denoted by a dot at the point of junction. Lines that cross but are not junctured are represented without a dot or by having a slight hump in one of the crossing lines at the crossing point.

Quick Couplings

Quick couplings allow fast installation and removal of components without having to use wrenches. Basically there are two types available and represented.

The quick couplings can be equipped with a mechanically opened non-return valve (check valve)

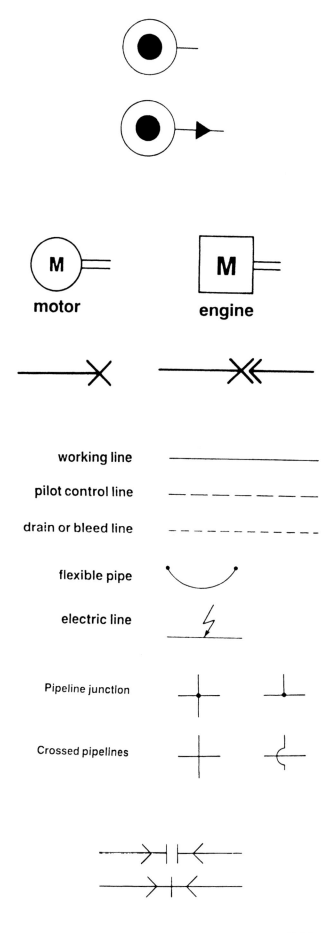

motor   engine

working line

pilot control line

drain or bleed line

flexible pipe

electric line

Pipeline junction

Crossed pipelines

or without a check valve. They can be drawn in pairs to represent a connected or unconnected condition; or singularly in the port of valve, as an example, to represent the method of junction to the circuit.

Rotary Connection

When a component(s) must rotate, the line(s) connecting is surrounded by a circular arrow. The number of lines passing through the circular arrow represents the number of flow paths, e.g. one way or three way.

Reservoirs

There are three styles of reservoirs: open, closed or sealed, and pressurized. The lines entering and leaving the reservoir are important in their positioning. If the line terminates above the fluid level, it is considered a drain or bleed line with low pressure and a small volume returning to tank. When the line is drawn below the fluid level to the bottom of the tank, this represents a suction or return line. A line that is drawn from the bottom and below the tank represents an overhead tank.

Pressurized tanks are completely closed to atmosphere, the lines entering and leaving the tank are shown the same as the open-to- atmosphere tank.

Accumulators

When an accumulator is used in a circuit, it can be a weight loaded, spring loaded, or compressed gas type. The accumulator stores fluid under pressure. The oval shape represents the vessel for storage. If the accumulator elements, such as inert gas and fluid are separated, there is a line drawn across the center of the oval.

The element that develops the pressure will be represented by a square for a weight loaded accumulator; a spring for a spring loaded accumulator; an open triangle for a compressed gas (nitrogen) accumulator.

Fluid Conditioners, Filters and Heat Exchangers

No matter what type of filter is used, the symbol is always the same. What determines if the filter is actually a sump strainer, suction filter, pressure, or a return filter is its location in the hydraulic circuit diagram.

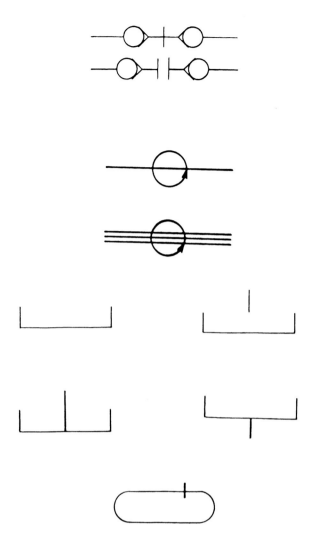

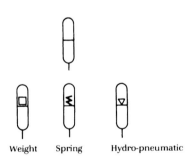

Weight   Spring   Hydro-pneumatic

Filter or strainer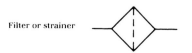

A temperature controller tries to maintain the fluid temperature between two predetermined limits. The arrows in the diamond indicate that heat may be induced or extracted as required.

Heat exchangers can either heat up, cool down, or maintain the temperature of the fluid. In the heater symbol, the arrows inside the diamond indicate the induction of heat to the circulating fluid. The cooler symbol can be represented in two ways. The arrows inside the diamond indicate the extraction of heat, but there is no representation of the type of coolant and coolant flow. Coolant can be either water or air as represented by the arrows for water flow outside the diamond.

Mechanical Components

There are a variety of control mechanisms used in controlling actuation of valve, cylinders, motor/pump, etc. These mechanisms can be of the mechanical, electrical, hydraulic or pneumatic type.

Rotating shafts, such as a pump shaft are represented by double parallel lines. The arrows indicate unidirectional or bi-directional rotation.

In some applications of directional valves it is desirable to mechanically hold the valve in one position. This is represented by the detent symbol. Detents can be spring loaded balls or spring loaded electromagnets; the symbol does not indicate the type being used.

Mechanical locking devices that can stop, as an example a conveyor, at various positions are controlled by some type of actuator that would be drawn inside the square. The actuator could be a solenoid.

Overcentering devices such as stroke limiter are used to prevent a valve spool from stopping on dead center position.

When a device is designed to pivot on an axis, the simplified symbol can represent this. However, when the devices have to traverse and/or have a fixed fulcrum point, the complete symbols are used.

Actuator Methods

The actuator symbols are incorporated into the component symbol that is being controlled. Depending upon which side of the component symbol the control symbol is adjacent to, the square is affected by actuation of the control.

Actuator methods can be manual (human) controls, mechanical controls, electrical controls, pressure controls, or a combination of two or more controls.

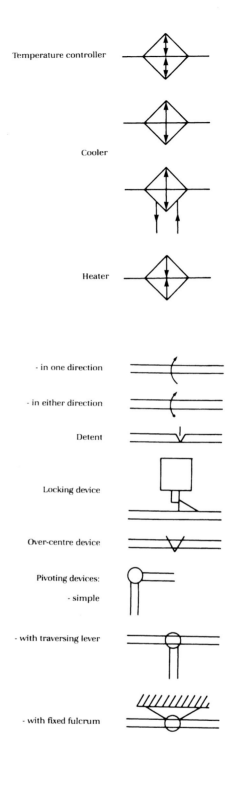

Temperature controller

Cooler

Heater

- in one direction

- in either direction

Detent

Locking device

Over-centre device

Pivoting devices:
- simple

- with traversing lever

- with fixed fulcrum

Manual Controls

The general symbol for manual (human effort) control doesn't indicate any specific type of control. There are pushbuttons or palm buttons, hand lever and foot pedal controls.

Mechanical Controls

Mechanical controls can be plunger or tracer, spring, roller for bidirection control, or a roller control that operates in only one direction.

Electrical Controls

Electrical controls most commonly used are solenoids. The diagonal line in the rectangle indicates a winding. A single diagonal line indicates the solenoid can operate in one direction and is directly connected to the device being controlled.

When the symbol is represented with two diagonal lines, it means the solenoid is capable of operating in both directions. If the double lines have an arrow drawn on a 45° slant through them, it means that the solenoid operates in a variable way progressively in both directions.

The other electrical control is the electric motor. A circle with an M inside indicates the motor, rotation is bidirectional as indicated by the double headed arrow, or unidirectional if arrow has only one head.

Another electrical symbol is the torque motor represented by two triangles, an arrow and a small circle.

Pressure Controls

Control of a component can be done by either applying pressure or releasing pressure. Direct acting control shows either hydraulic or pneumatic pressure being applied directly to the square. Also, hydraulic or pneumatic pressure could be released directly from the square.

Control can be accomplished by different size control areas. The larger rectangle on the left represents the priority phase of the control.

Indirect control symbols indicate pilot operated directonal control valves. Pressure comes into the rectangle in the form of hydraulic or pneumatic pressure and can be released from the rectangle.

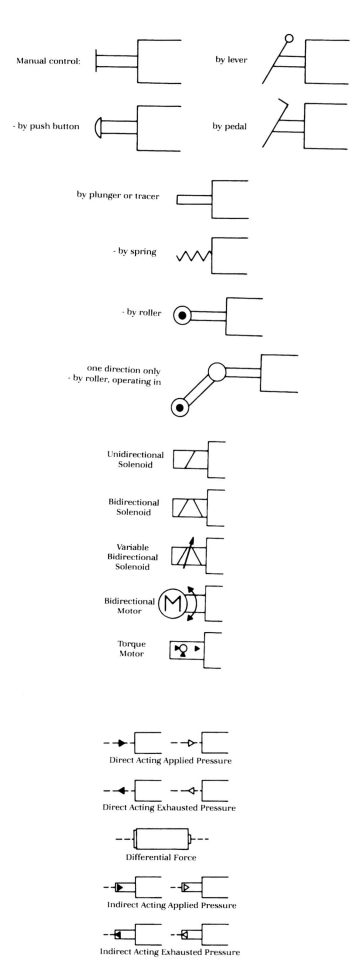

Manual control: by lever

- by push button   by pedal

by plunger or tracer

- by spring

- by roller

- by roller, operating in one direction only

Unidirectional Solenoid

Bidirectional Solenoid

Variable Bidirectional Solenoid

Bidirectional Motor

Torque Motor

Direct Acting Applied Pressure

Direct Acting Exhausted Pressure

Differential Force

Indirect Acting Applied Pressure

Indirect Acting Exhausted Pressure

Combined Controls

By combining two or more control symbols we can simplify, for example, the symbol for a solenoid controlled, pilot operated, spring centered directional valve. The pilot valve is controlled by the solenoid, the main valve would be controlled by pressure and springs.

If a valve can be controlled by either a solenoid or pressure, the control symbols are stacked.

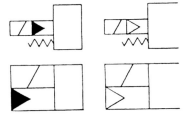

Miscellaneous Equipment

In a hydraulic circuit, pressure, temperature and flow must be measured.

To measure either pressure or vacuum, a pressure gauge is installed. To represent the point of installation, a line is drawn to the circle. The arrow in the inside of the circle indicates pressure or vacuum. The location of this symbol in the circuit diagram will determine if it is pressure or vacuum that is being measured.

Temperature of the hydraulic fluid can be measured with a thermometer. The symbol is similar to a pressure gauge except for the thermometer symbol inside the circle.

The flow rate out of the pump or into and out of any component or leg of a hydraulic circuit is measured with a flow meter or an integrating flow meter.

Another often used symbol is the electric pressure switch. The dashed line is hydraulic pressure that actuates the switch, the spring holds the switch in either a normally passing or normally non-passing condition. Over the contact points you may find NO or NC to represent whether the switch is normally open or closed.

Some springs are shown as variable by placing an arrow on a 45° slant through the spring.

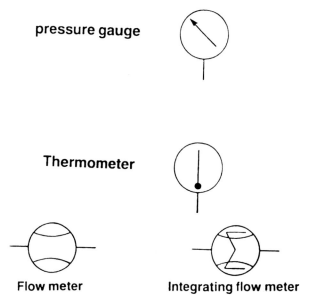

pressure gauge

Thermometer

Flow meter   **Integrating flow meter**

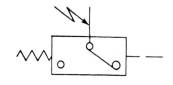

Mechanical Feedback Control

In applications such as a copying control, the mechanical connection between the controlling apparatus' moving part and the controlled apparatus is represented by this symbol: 1 = controlled apparatus, 2 = control apparatus.

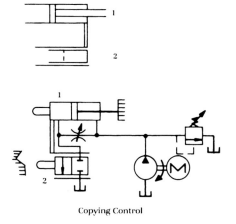

Copying Control

EXERCISE - Hydraulic Graphic Symbology

1. Develop a power-out, power-back circuit using a double acting cylinder. Circuit control is electrical. The cylinder is capable of stopping anywhere along its travel and holding the load whenever the controls are released.

   a. In Figure 1, the cylinder size is 5 inch bore, 2 inch rod and 30 inch stroke. The cylinder speed is 20 feet per minute and the maximum load being moved is 32,000 lbs. Indicate the various line connections in the circuit and place an "X" at all unused ports.

   b. How many gallons per minute are required to maintain the rod speed?

   _____

   c. What is the required working pressure for the circuit?

   _____

   d. Complete Figure 1A by drawing in the graphic symbols that represent this circuit.

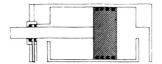

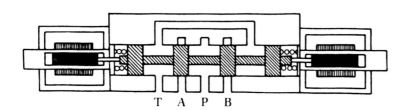

T A P B

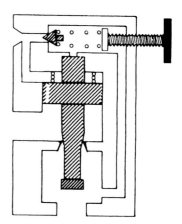

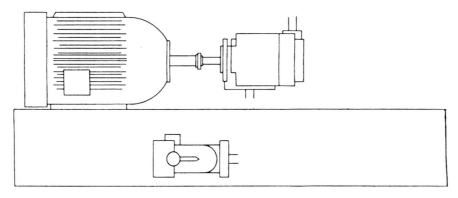

Figure 1

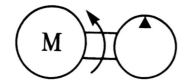

Figure 1A

2.   If the speed of an actuator must be precise throughout the workday, flow control devices must be used. In some cases, the work load changes causing the cylinder to speed up or slow down. To help the control

   a.   Indicate the various line connections in the circuit and place an "X" at all unused ports in Figure 2.

   b.   What is the common name for this type of circuit?

   _____

   _____

   c.   Complete Figure 2A by drawing in the graphic symbols that represent this circuit.

   d.   With relief valve set for 2000 psi, pump output is 15 GPM, cylinder is a 7 inch bore, rod is 3 inch diameter and flow control valve is adjusted to a 6 GPM flow rate. How much heat generation is there and how can we eliminate this problem?

   _____

   _____

   _____

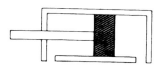

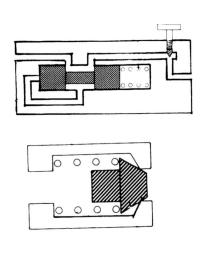

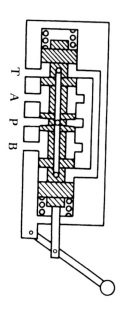

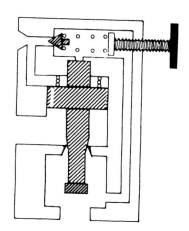

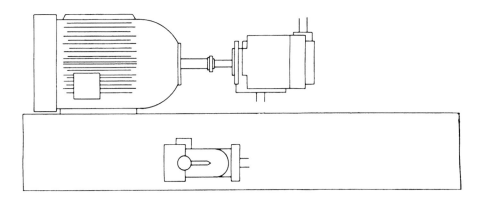

Figure 2

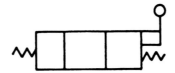

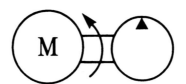

Figure 2A

3. Another type of flow control circuit can be used to control the speed of a cylinder. Besides generating less heat than the previous circuit, it can also be more economical than either a meter-in or meter-out circuit.

    a. The common name for this circuit is?

    _____

    _____

    b. Indicate the various line connections in the circuit and place an "X" at all unused ports in Figure 3.

    c. Give the complete nomenclature of the directional control valve and what benefit is derived by using this type of D. C. valve.

    _____

    _____

    _____

    d. Complete Figure 3A by drawing the graphic symbols that represent this circuit.

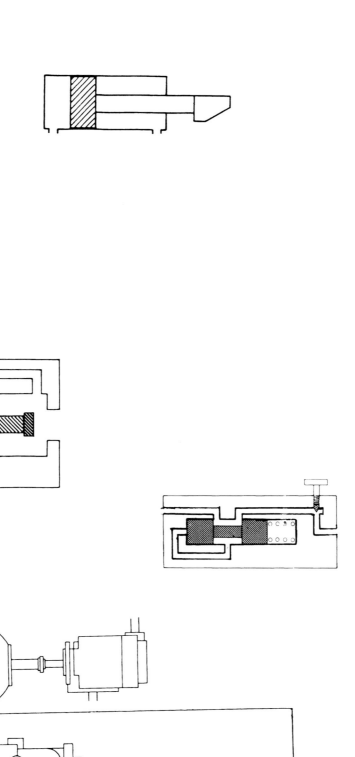

Figure 3

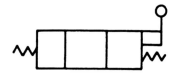

Figure 3A

4. When a circuit has a long idle period in the "at rest" position, it is desirable to unload the pump automtically.

    a. Draw lines to connect the ports so that when the cylinder is in the fully retracted position, the pump will automatically unload. Place an "X" at all unused ports in Figure 4.

    b. Complete Figure 4A by drawing the graphic symbols that represent this circuit.

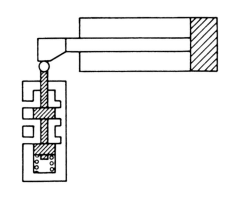

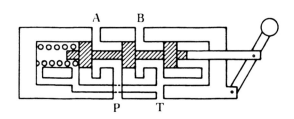

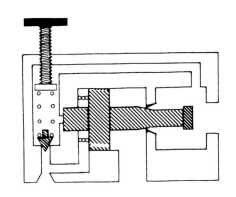

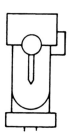

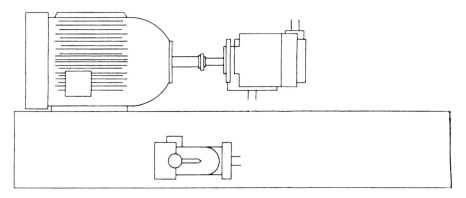

Figure 4

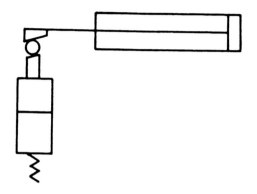

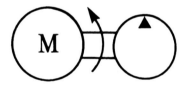

Figure 4A

5. In the circuit illustrated, cylinder A must work at a maximum pressure of 2500 psi. Cylinder B should not exceed 1500 psi when working. When the machine is idle and doing no work, the pump should be unloaded. Cylinder A and B operate independent of one another.

   a. Connect the components in Figure 5 so that the above conditions are met. Place an "X" at all unused ports.

   b. Describe in detail the type of relief valve used.

   _____

   _____

   c. What is the best way to set the pressures of the relief valve?

   _____

   _____

   _____

   _____

   d. Complete Figure 5A by drawing the graphic symbols that represent this circuit.

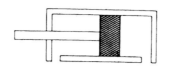

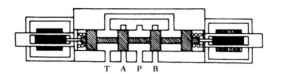

T A P B

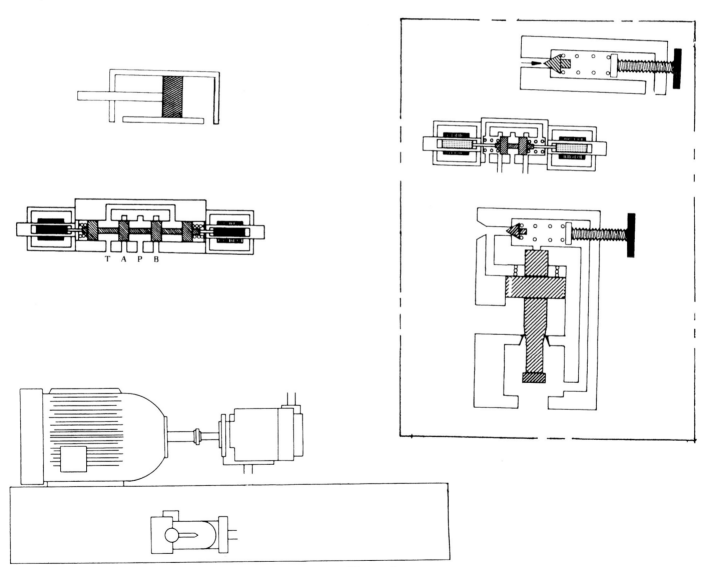

Figure 5

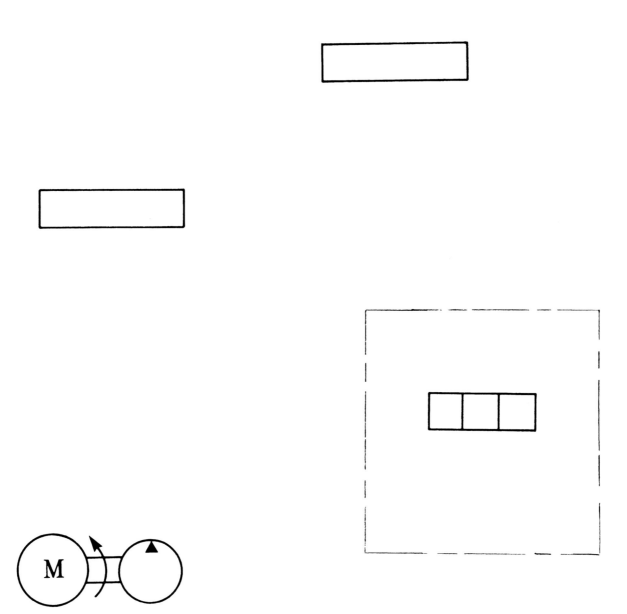

Figure 5A

6. The regenerative circuit which is illustrated consists of a pump, relief valve, directional valve and a 2:1 cylinder.

    a. Draw the various line connections in the circuit and place an "X" at all unused ports in Figure 6.

    b. When the circuit is in the regeneration mode, what is sacrificed in the circuit?

_____

_____

    c. Describe in detail, the type of directional control valve used and what is meant by "2:1 cylinder."

_____

_____

    d. What would happen to the circuit if one cylinder began to bypass internally?

_____

_____

_____

_____

    e. How do you check for an internal leak at one or both cylinders?

_____

_____

_____

_____

_____

_____

    f. Complete Figure 6A by drawing the graphic symbols that represent this circuit.

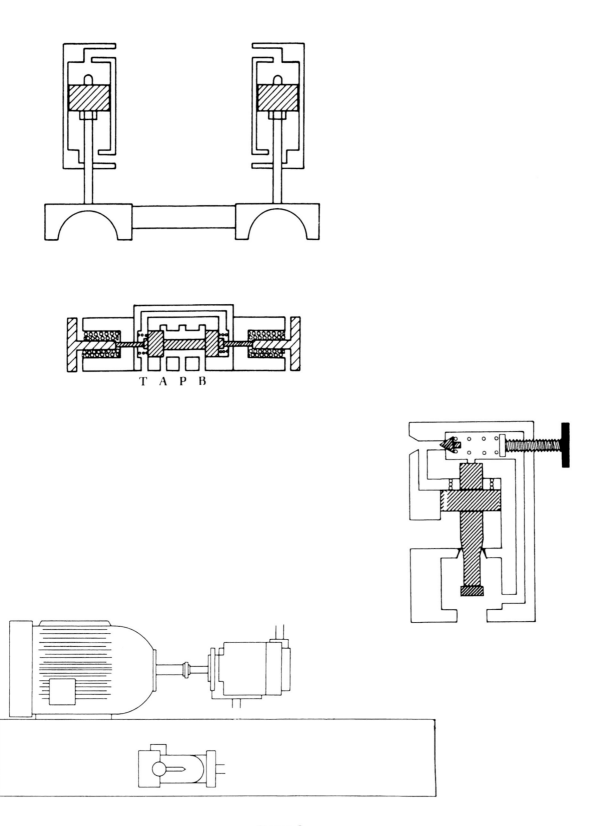

Figure 6

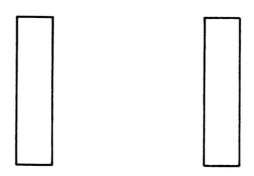

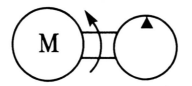

Figure 6A

7. In this circuit, a rapid traverse of 300 in/min is needed until the machining portion of the stroke is reached. Then a slow feed of 100 in/min is required. At the end of the machining process a rapid retraction of 500 in/min is needed to get into position for the next cycle.

   a. Connect the components in Figure 7 so that the above conditions are met. Place an "X" at all unused ports.

   b. The cylinder bore is a 4" diameter and the rod diameter is 2.." What is the GPM requirement of the pump?

   c. Complete Figure 7A by drawing in the graphic symbols that represent this circuit.

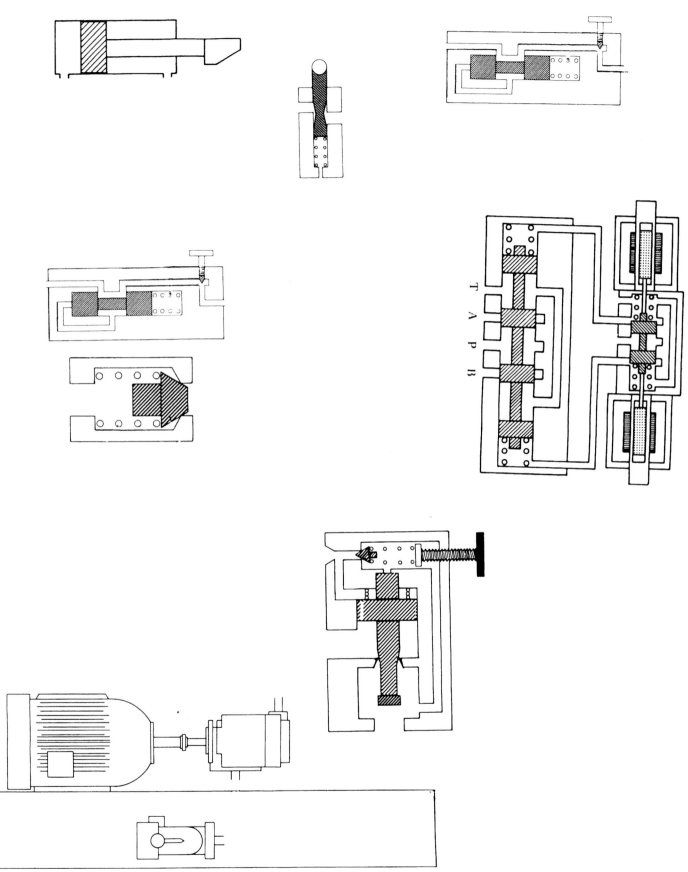

Figure 7

Figure 7A

POWER UNIT MAINTENANCE

There is more to a standard hydraulic power unit than meets the eye. It is a complex energy system that consists of the reservoir, electric motor, pump/motor coupling, pump, possibly an inlet filter and/or strainer, filter/breather, pressure relief valve, gage(s), directional control valve(s), mounting plate or pad, motor starter box, oil level gage, temperature gage, baffling, fittings, etc.

Hydraulic Reservoir

Industrial reservoirs come in a variety of styles. The four general styles are: standard (JIC), L-shaped, vertical and overhead.

The standard reservoir is the most commonly used industrial style. Let us examine the construction of the reservoir first.

Reservoir Construction

As an example, a 10-gallon (38 liter) reservoir would be made of 11 gage steel for the bottom and sides; 7 gage for the ends; and 3/8 inch (9.5 mm) thick steel for the top. Though the manufacturer decides these things, it is an important fact in preventing collapse of the reservoir walls under operating conditions.

It can be coated with anti-corrosion material on the inside and outside. However, it is advised that the compatability between these materials and the system fluid should be checked before using them in the system. Some manufacturers are beginning to use stainless steel to

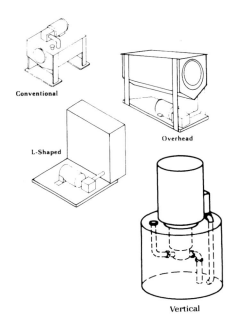

Conventional

L-Shaped

Overhead

Vertical

eliminate the need for interior and exterior coatings. In this way, a system can have its fluid changed, as an example, from petroleum base fluid to high water content fluid, without concern for tank interior condition.

There are two common construction methods -- welded all around and welded sides and bolted and gasketed top. The former is found used with standard and submerged pump types and the latter with L-shaped and overhead types.

Component Mounting

It is customary on standard reservoirs to mount the electric motor, pump and valve(s) on a separate, rigid mounting plate. This plate in turn is attached to the top of the reservoir with stand-off feet. This method allows use of some of the top area of the reservoir for fluid cooling by allowing air flow across the top and this method also prevents direct generation of vibration in the tank top.

Reservoir Add-ons

Located in the top plate of the standard reservoir are tubes for return fluid line, drain fluid line, suction line and filter/breather.

At either end of the tank or at both ends is a clean-out cover, drain plug and fluid level indicator. The filter/breather is located at either end of the reservoir. As a maintenance point, these four items should always be located at the same end of the reservoir. Many times the reservoir is located so there is only one side convenient to approach for servicing.

The bottom plate of the reservoir should slope or have a dished shape. This minimizes sediment collecting in corners when the reservoir is drained periodically.

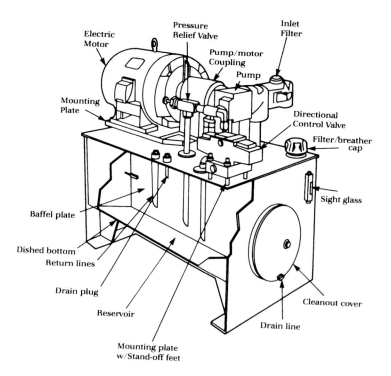

3-2

Reservoir Interior

The reservoir should contain internal baffling to separate newly returned fluid from the pump suction line. This allows more sediment settling time for the return fluid and more air is able to escape from the fluid. It also tends to make the fluid take less of a turbulent path from return to suction giving the fluid a chance to give up trapped air and contaminants. This helps to eliminate aeration of the pump inlet. The overall construction of the reservoir is designed, as seen, to help in the prevention of some common problems, e.g. overheating, aeration and contamination.

Electric Motors

Mounted on the mounting plate, on top of the reservoir, is the electric motor. Electrical power as it is delivered to a system, under the form of voltage and current, is transformed into rotary mechanical power by the electric motor and passed on to a pump.

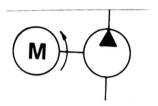

3-Phase Squirrel Cage Induction Motor

Because of its simplicity and low cost, a common electric motor for an industrial hydraulic system is a 3-phase, squirrel cage induction motor.

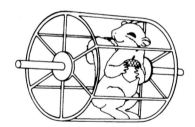

All 3-phase, squirrel cage induction motors are not the same. Depending on the design of the rotor and the induced magnetic field, operating characteristics will vary. For the sake of standardization members of the National Electrical Manufacturers Association (NEMA) working with industrial users decided that four designs would satisfy industrial needs. These designs are labeled "A," "B," "C" or "D" with the design "B" being seen most frequently in industrial systems. The actual class definitions are the following:

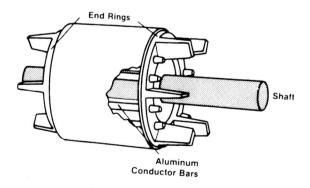

End Rings

Shaft

Aluminum
Conductor Bars

Squirrel Cage Rotor

- NEMA Class A - A general purpose motor with starting currents 5 to 7 times rated and starting torque 150% rated.

- NEMA Class B - A general purpose motor with starting current 4.5 to 5 times rated, starting torque 150% rated.

- NEMA Class C - A double squirrel cage motor with high starting torque characteristics. Starting current 4.5 to 5 times rated, torque 225% rated.

- NEMA Class D - High torque, high resistance motor, with starting current 4 to 4.5 times rated and starting torque 275% rated. There are also classes "E" and "F." However, these are little used since nearly all applications are usually met better by the other classes.

NEMA Speed Rating

A speed-torque performance curve for a NEMA "B" design motor points out a motor's synchronous and full-load speeds. Speed (RPM) of a squirrel cage motor depends on line frequency and the number of poles in the motor stator. With 3-phase power and a line frequency of 60 Hz, squirrel cage motors with four (4) poles operate at 1800 RPM and motors with six (6) poles run at 1200 RPM.

Speeds of 1200 RPM for a six (6) pole motor and 1800 RPM for a four (4) pole motor are known as synchronous speeds which means the rotor is turning at the same pace as the rotating magnetic field in the stator. In actuality this does not occur, the rotor turns slower than synchronous speed.

A motor turning at slightly less than synchronous speed under no-load condition, will deviate from synchronous speed to a greater extent as load increases. The difference between synchronous speed and the speed of the motor as it is loaded is known as "slip."

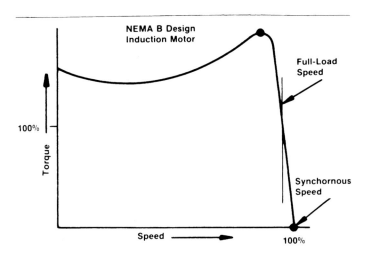

Synchronous Vs. Full-Load RPM

HP	Synchronous RPM	Full-Load RPM	HP	Synchronous RPM	Full-Load RPM
½	900	850	25	3,600	3,525
¾	1,200	1,140		1,800	1,765
	900	850		1,200	1,170
				900	875
1	1,800	1,735	30	3,600	3,530
	1,200	1,140		1,800	1,750
	900	870		1,200	1,165
1½	3,600	3,475		900	875
	1,800	1,715	40	3,600	3,530
	1,200	1,160		1,800	1,755
	900	865		1,200	1,170
2	3,600	3,495		900	875
	1,800	1,725	50	3,600	3,545
	1,200	1,155		1,800	1,760
	900	865		1,200	1,170
3	3,600	3,510		900	875
	1,800	1,745	60	3,600	3,545
	1,200	1,160		1,800	1,770
	900	865		1,200	1,175
5	3,600	3,510		900	875
	1,800	1,745	75	3,600	3,555
	1,200	1,150		1,800	1,770
	900	860		1,200	1,175
7½	3,600	3,530		900	880
	1,800	1,755	100	3,600	3,550
	1,200	1,155		1,800	1,775
	900	860		1,200	1,175
10	3,600	3,520		900	880
	1,800	1,750	125	3,600	3,560
	1,200	1,155		1,800	1,780
	900	870		1,200	1,175
15	3,600	3,520	150	3,600	3,560
	1,800	1,750		1,800	1,770
	1,200	1,170			
	900	870	200	3,600	3,560
20	3,600	3,520		1,800	1,770
	1,800	1,750			
	1,200	1,170	250	3,600	3,560
	900	875			

Slip of a squirrel cage motor is generally less than 5% at full load. It is common to refer to these as constant speed motors since at full load, speed varies little.

Motor Enclosure Type

A motor is enclosed to protect its vital internal parts from damage due to its environment, while others protect a potentially explosive atmosphere from igniting by enclosing the motor to prevent ignition. The different types of enclosures are:

- Open - One having ventilating openings for free air cooling.

- Drip-proof - Constructed so that drops of liquid falling on the motor at an angle of 15° or less from vertical cannot enter. This is intended for indoor location where the air is fairly clean.

- Guarded - Ventilated openings are limited to specific size and shape to prevent insertion of fingers or rods to avoid accidental contact with rotating or electrical parts.

- Splash-proof - Ventilation openings are constructed so that drops of solids falling on the motor at an angle less than 100° from the vertical will not enter this motor. It is intended for more severe service than the drip-proof. If better protection is needed, the trend is toward drip-proof with sealed insulation or a totally enclosed motor.

- Weather Protected Type 1 - An open motor designed to minimize the entrance of rain, snow or other particles and prevent the passage of a cylindrical rod of 3/4″ diameter. The housing is similar to the drip-proof, with the addition of outdoor type bearings, sealed insulation and screens on ventilation openings.

- Weather Protected Type 2 - In addition to the type 1, the air flow entering the motor is baffled to prevent airborne particles from contacting the electrical media.

- Totally Enclosed - This type of enclosure prevents the free exchange of air between the inside and outside of the case but is not airtight.

- Totally Enclosed Non-Ventilated (TENV) - Totally enclosed motor with no means of cooling the enclosed parts. It is restricted to small motor sizes.

- Totally Enclosed Fan Cooled (TEFC) - Motors equipped with an exterior fan internal to the motor, external to the enclosed parts. The external fan spreads a blanket of air on the totally enclosed motor frame helping to dissipate heat. This enclosure is popular in dusty, dirty and corrosive atmospheres.

- Encapsulated - An open motor whose windings are covered with a heavy coating of material to protect them from moisture, dirt and abrasion. If the coils are totally en- capsulated, this motor can be used in applications where only totally enclosed motors were employed.

- Explosion proof - Designed to prevent ignition of gas or vapor surrounding the motor. It is evident that the motor is impervious to the elements surrounding it.

NEMA Frame Size

A standard system has been adopted for frame sizes of motors up to 500 HP at 1800 RPM. This is followed by most companies manufacturing motors. This frame number standardizes certain motor mounting dimensions.

Previously, frame sizes were designated by letters. The two most common were "U" and "T" frame motors. A "U" frame motor consisted of a heavier frame than the comparable "T." With the heavy "U" frame, the motor could be intermittently overloaded longer because of its heavy mass giving it a higher thermal capacity. In this way, the motor would not overheat. This type is still used for heavy duty applications such as in steel mills and automotive plants.

Electric Motor and Pump Coupling

Electric motors in combination with hydraulic pumps develop hydraulic power. To perform this function, pump and electric motor are coupled together at their shafts.

Rigid Coupling

The simplest shaft coupling consists of a metal sleeve with set screws. The sleeve fits over the two shafts and set screws are tightened to form the mechanical connection. This is known as a rigid coupling.

Rigid couplings have disadvantages in that the shafts which are joined must have their axes in perfect alignment. If they are not, pump and electric motor shaft bearings and seals on the pump may be severely damaged due to the side loading that occurs. The use of this type coupling, even if the shafts are perfectly aligned, will not allow for thermal expansion as they system is brought up to working temperature. The coefficient of expansion may be such that tremendous loading forces may be imposed on the rotating groups (bearings, housing, etc.) of both the pump and electric motor. This would shorten the service life of both significantly.

Flexible Coupling

To minimize the effects of shaft misalignment and other associated problems, pump and electric motor are commonly joined with a flexible coupling. Flexible couplings allow shafts to be slightly out of alignment while transmitting power. They are capable of allowing for thermal expansion when the system is at operat-

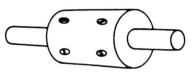
Rigid Coupling

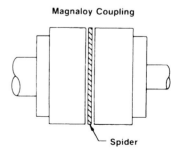
Magnaloy Coupling

Spider

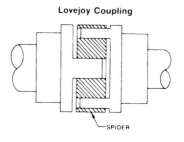
Lovejoy Coupling

SPIDER

ing temperature range, and they are capable of compensating for end play of an electric motor.

Some common couplings include the Lovejoy, Magnaloy and chain.

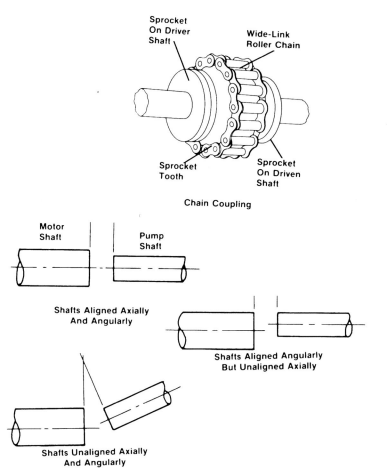

Chain Coupling

Shaft Alignment

If pump and electric motor alignment is not maintained within manufacturer's specifications the shaft side loading which can result could cause shaft seals and bearings of both pump and electric motor to fail prematurely.

Alignment must be maintained axially and angularly with sufficient space between coupling halves to allow for thermal expansion and end play from the electric motor. End play is the amount of axial movement experienced at a motor shaft as it is accelerated from an "at rest" condition to operating speed.

Dial Indicator Installation

To minimize side loading the bearings and shaft seals, and to ensure longer coupling life with quieter operation, the electric motor and pump shafts must be aligned to within .003″ Total Indicator Reading (T.I.R.). Every good maintenance person has their own pet method of shaft alignment. To begin the procedure with foot-mounted pump - motor alignment, a straight edge and feeler gage can be used to get the alignment into a "ballpark" range. Then install a dial indicator, as illustrated, for the precision alignment required.

Shimming Requirements

With the dial indicator installed and the shafts rotated together, the indicator can be set to the zero position. Readings should be taken at all positions, rotating the shafts together. The T.I.R. should not exceed .003″ in one complete rotation of the shafts. Half of the T.I.R. is the shimming required on the pump or motor for

the required shaft height centerpoint alignment. A second indicator can be installed on the opposing shaft for greater accuracy and expedience. Illustrated is a graph that will aid you in the shimming procedure.

NOTE: This shimming procedure is usually done when the system is cold. It should be repeated after the system has run hot to compensate for minor distortion due to expansion.

Shaft End-play Clearance

Shaft end loading can be very detrimental to both pump and electric motor bearings. Due to operational friction, the shaft temperatures will increase and both the pump and motor shafts will expand, closing up the end clearance.

The clearance is measured, as shown, between the coupling halves. The total clearance, "A" + "B," is to be no less than 1/8 inch and no greater than 1/4 inch.

Angular alignment between the coupling halves should also be checked. This is accomplished by making a face check which ensures that the coupling faces are parallel. On small coupling gaps, face checks can be performed with feeler gages. On large gaps, inside micrometers or a dial indicator can be used.

Measurements for a face check are made between the coupling halves at 90° intervals at points equi-distant from the shaft radius.

When are Alignment Checks Required

Shaft alignment between pump and electric motor should be checked. Anytime a machine has been relocated even if the distance moved is very short. Whenever piping connections have been changed or altered in their mounting arrangements, the rigidity of the piping can cause the pump alignment to be altered

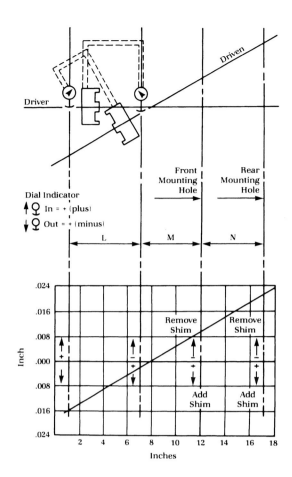

due to pressures within the piping causing the piping to move, or due to thermal expansion of the piping. Whenever a pump or electric motor has been replaced, alignment is needed.

Alignment should be checked whenever increasing noise levels are detected from the pump or electric motor.

Although power unit, fabricators align pump and motor shafts with precision care at their plant, this alignment may be altered in shipment to you.

Pump Mounting

Once pump and electric motor shafts are aligned within specifications, the goal is to maintain the alignment. This can be aided by the type of pump mounting. Generally, pumps are either flange (bell housing) or foot mounted. Flange mounted pumps are highly recommended because the alignment and coupling halves end clearance have been machined into the precision made mounting flange. This bell housing adapter makes the pump and electric motor an integral unit which can more easily ward off misalignment problems.

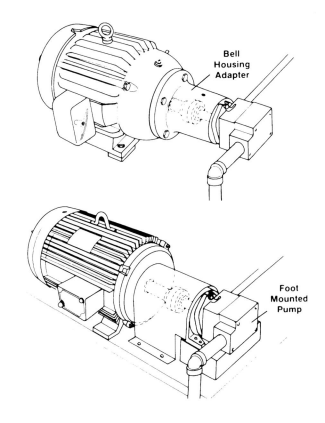

Bell Housing Adapter

Foot Mounted Pump

In many instances, mainly for flexibility of electric motor and/or pump replacement, the foot mounted pump arrangement is preferred.

NOTE: If electric motor or pump replacement is a frequent occurrence, there may be something wrong. The hydraulic and electrical systems should be checked for possible malfunctions.

Foot mounts are equipped with a base which is bolted to a rigid mounting plate, if installed on top of the reservoir. The mounting plate bolts down to solid riser blocks welded to the reservoir. Pump risers come in various lengths and dimensions to accommodate the necessary mounting height requirements of the pump to the electric motor. These riser blocks will not flex or distort with temperature changes, nor will they vibrate when the pump is operated.

Mounting Base Plate

For top of the reservoir mounting, boiler plate is commonly used as the mounting base plate. Because reservoirs distort with temperature, the level of the fluid in the reservoir, how level the floor location is, and weight of the fluid in the reservoir, the pump and electric motor shaft alignment would be affected if mounted directly to the reservoir.

The mounting plate thickness and weight should be compatible with pump and electric motor size to maintain alignment stability.

Start-up Procedure

Assuming that a power unit has been correctly assembled with the right components, the pump-motor shaft alignment is within specifications, all electrical connections and safety devices are correct, the system should be ready to start.

First step is to check the fluid. Is there too much, too little or no fluid in the reservoir? Is this the correct type fluid and is it clean (reference Preventive Maintenance section)? When a new power unit or system is installed, fill the reservoir to the "high" full mark. When placing only a pump or other component, fill reservoir to "low" mark.

Step 2 - is to prime the pump. The pump case should be filled with the same fluid as in the reservoir by removing the case drain line or case fill plug if so equipped, or by removing either the inlet or outlet line.

Step 3 - would be to install a vacuum gage and pressure gages. At the inlet a vacuum gage or manometer filled with mercury (Hg) is required to check for the proper inlet specification as determined by the pump manufacturer.

As a rule of thumb, the vacuum reading should not be greater than 10″ Hg for gear and vane pumps and not greater than 3″ Hg for piston pumps. But again, the pump manufacturer should be consulted for exact limits.

Pressure gages should be installed in the system to monitor pump pressure build-up as well as system pressure.

Some manufacturers of variable displacement pumps with a case drain port usually have specific recommendations on the amount of allowable backpressure and flow through this port. Monitoring this pressure and flow can give a good indication of pump operating condition.

Step 4 - requires the system pressure relief valve or dump valve to be backed out so that pump output bypasses through the valve at low pressure. This allows air to be pushed out from the pump case through the outlet back to the tank where it will dissipate to the atmosphere.

Step 5 - start the pump and let it run for several minutes under this no-load condition. While pump is running, make a visual check for external leaks and listen for strange and unusual noises.

Step 6 - after several minutes of successful operation in the no-load condition, pressure can be slowly increased toward rated system pressure. As an example, adjust pressure to 1/4 of system pressure and run at that setting for 5-10 minutes. Again, check for unusual noises and leaks. Adjust pressure to 1/2 of system maximum pressure and run at that setting 5-10 minutes again checking for unusual noises, leaks and operating temperature. Continue this stepping procedure until maximum pressure has been reached. When pressure compensated pumps are being adjusted in this step, the compensator is turned in as far as possible. This allows only the system relief valve to control system pressure.

It should be understood that the relief valve in a pressure compensated pump system serves as a back up to the compensator valve. The pressure settings between the compensator and the relief valve should have a pressure spread of 250 to 300 psi to eliminate "hunting" of the compensator mechanism.

CAUTION: During this step, always be watchful of the fluid temperature. Do not exceed manufacturer's operating temperature recommendations.

Step 7 - if there are no unusual noises or leaks, recheck fluid level in reservoir and if needed, add fluid to bring level up to the full of "high" mark in the sight gage while system is running.

NOTE: If at any time during this start-up procedure, should noises, leaks and/or high operating temperatures occur, shut down the power unit and correct the problem.

Noise

Noise as defined by Webster's dictionary, is a disturbance interfering with the operation of a mechanical device or system. But to the human ear, noise is any sound that is uncomfortable and unwanted.

Noise in the power unit is viewed as an ecology and performance problem. As an ecology problem, the Federal Government has set maximum decibel ratings that an employee can be exposed to for an eight-hour day. As a performance problem, the noise generated by a power unit can be the sign of an impending component failure or improper component installation.

How we Hear Internal Noise from a Hydraulic System

Even though the fluid is enclosed in the pump, valves and lines, we still can hear the noise made by the fluid passing into and through these components. This noise is in the form of sound waves which are transmitted through the metal housings, then through the air to our ears. We also hear sound waves produced by mechanical parts, such as sliding pump vanes, large panels of the reservoir, etc.

Some mechanical parts such as large and thin panels actually amplify or magnify sound waves from internal disturbances so they sound unusually loud. Many noise sound waves when added together will sound much louder (more intense) than any one individual noise sound wave.

Also, the mechanical pump-motor coupling and the electric motor, usually including a cooling fan and shroud, must be considered integral parts of the overall noise generating, transmitting and amplifying process.

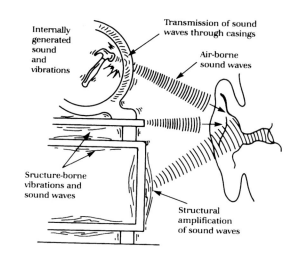

Noise in the Hydraulic Pump

Most of the noise in a hydraulic pump is created by fluid that changes pressure rapidly. The more drastic the pressure change, the amount of fluid involved, and the more rapidly the change occurs, the higher will be the pump noise level.

In all pumps, there is an increase in fluid pressure in the cavity known as the compression zone, that is moving fluid the inlet to the outlet port. In this compression zone, an improperly designed pump will build pressure too rapidly, thus making more noise. Ideally, the pressure rise will be gradual over the entire zone producing very little noise.

In all positive displacement pumps, (vane, gear and piston), most noise is generated by the recombining of fluids at the outlet port. The noise is greatest when the pressure of fluid in the pump compression chamber is not as high as the system line pressure when they meet. The rapid pressure change (causing noise) occurs as backwash, that is, where the higher line pressure rushes back into the oncoming chamber, compressing the volume of fluid in the chamber up to line pressure. If pump chamber pressure is raised to precisely the line pressure, then there should be only insignificant recombining noise.

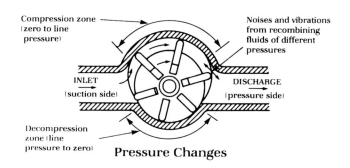

Pressure Changes

A pump will also be noisy if chamber pressure is higher than line pressure. In this case, there will be a rapid pressure drop causing noise in the outlet port area as the chamber opens to the discharge pressure.

Another area where noise can occur from changing fluid pressures is in the decompression zone. Trapped fluids must be reduced to zero pressure as the vanes, gears or pistons return to the suction or inlet side of the pump. This pressure transition must be gradual or else loud noises will be generated by too sudden a pressure drop. Compression and decompression pressure changes at the pump outlet port also set up what is called a "pressure ripple."

How Pressure Ripples Generate Noise

When pressure ripples occur, they themselves only generate a slight amount of noise. However, the vibrations that are a result can affect the entire hydraulic system and associated machine. A minor shock wave is sent through the system with the passing of each volume of oil through the outlet port. This is followed by a pressure decay; hence, a repeating cycle of pressure waves is established.

When the ripple frequency combines with the natural frequency of the machine, the amplitude and any resulting noise will be increased.

Other Noises Generated by the Pump

Other noises of significant importance generated by the pump comes from mechanical noises and vibration.

The rapid compressions and violent decompressions cause many simultaneous reactions. The housing itself is momentarily deflected then returns to normal. Both the expansion and contraction of the metal causes noise. These phenomena create a sound wave in the metal

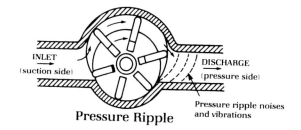

INLET (suction side)   DISCHARGE (pressure side)

Pressure ripple noises and vibrations

Pressure Ripple

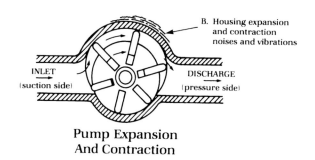

B. Housing expansion and contraction noises and vibrations

INLET (suction side)   DISCHARGE (pressure side)

Pump Expansion And Contraction

which is transmitted through the air to our ears.

There is the effect of misalignment between pump and electric motor shafts, the main cause of vibrations in the hydraulic system. There is also the effect of pressure peaks and decays which cause a slight slowing and speeding up of the pump shaft which causes vibrations. These strong rotational vibrations are transmitted through the pump housing to the entire system.

NOTE: If any of the system components happen to be on the same frequency, a resonance will be set up whereby the entire power unit will vibrate much more than normal.

Violent Changes in Fluid Velocity Make Noise

In order to understand how violent changes in fluid velocity make noise, we must examine two types of flows.

Laminar flow - through a conductor has fluid particles moving smoothly along parallel paths with only slight friction or drag at the pipe walls.

Turbulent flow - through a conductor shows a marked increase in random particle movement along the pipe or housing walls. This increased molecular interaction causes sounds which are transmitted through the walls of the conductor. The higher the fluid velocity, the greater the molecular activity and the louder the noise.

Extremely turbulent flow results when a flow restriction is encountered which increases flow velocity. Restrictions usually are in the form of valves, fittings and any sharp change in flow direction. The sudden changes in flow direction cause a phenomena known as cavitation to occur which cause noise in the piping or valving. Industrial hydraulic systems are considered very turbulent because of their many sharp turns in pumps, valves, etc. and high velocity flows.

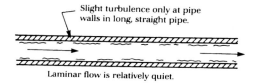

Slight turbulence only at pipe walls in long, straight pipe.

Laminar flow is relatively quiet.

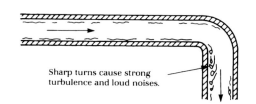

Sharp turns cause strong turbulence and loud noises.

Turbulence can also occur in the inlet of pumps as well as the outlet. The drastic changes in diameter and flow path are important contributors, but the violent compression/decompression action causes the greatest sound waves. These are transmitted through the metal casings, then through the air to our ears, exactly as turbulence in pipes.

Internal valves in pumps also induce turbulence. Some designs also chatter at certain flow velocities.

There are still other turbulences created at the pump inlet that cause noise within the pump.

Aeration and Cavitation Cause Noise

Within the pump inlet two phenomena can occur individually and jointly. Both will cause noise, heat, pressure fluctuation, vibration and severe pump damage.

Aeration is caused by outside air being drawn into the fluid stream entering the pump inlet. As the air bubbles enter the pump's compression zone, they are subjected to an increase in pressure. This sudden action causes the air pressure inside the bubble to increase until it bursts, generating loud noise and vibrations.

Air bubbles explode at start of compression zone causing loud noises.

Other detrimental effects to the pump would be excessive heat caused by a lack of lubrication and the heat created by compression of the air bubbles causing the pump metal to break down, become soft and flake or chip away.

The other phenomenon is cavitation. This occurs due to a severe restriction within the pump suction line.

Cavitation bubbles are actually liquid vapor bubbles caused by a lack of absolute pressure on the surface of the liquid within the suction line. As these vapor cavities enter the compression zone of the pump, they are subjected to an in-

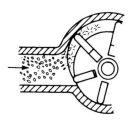

Cavitation bubbles collapse back into suspension at start of compression zone causing loud noises.

crease in pressure. At the inlet, these bubbles implode generating a very distinguishable, high pitched, continuous noise which may or may not be heard over the other plant noises. Because these implosions occur very rapidly and develop tremendous forces, the pump walls and pumping elements that are exposed to this will show severe signs of pitting and other areas will show excessive wear due to a lack of lubrication.

Noise within other hydraulic components such as valves, motors and cylinders can also be caused by aeration and/or cavitation occurring.

Noise from Pressure Control Valves

Pressure control valves can generate noise of both mechanical and hydraulic type. Squealing sounds are the result of high flow velocity turbulence and cavitation in narrow passages.

Metal to metal chatter can occur when pressure controls are used in series and/or their pressure settings are too close to one another. As an example, a pressure compensated pump's compensator and secondary relief valve settings have only a 100 psi differential. At least 250 psi is recommended.

Other Noises Associated with the Power Unit

The pump and valve noise generation basically arises from the vibrations of surfaces in contact with air bubbles or vapor cavities. Noise transmission exists when sound waves generated from one component set up vibrations in other components. Such as the reservoir receives significant vibrations generated by the pump, valves, coupling, electric motor, fan, etc., via structure-borne transmission. The reservoir then acts like a large amplifier.

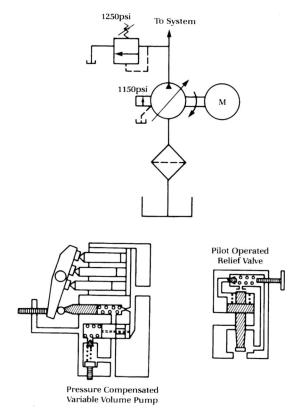

1250psi To System

1150psi M

Pressure Compensated
Variable Volume Pump

Pilot Operated
Relief Valve

Noise amplification (magnification) occurs when sound waves are increased due to the surface of material it comes in contact with. For example, an alarm clock hanging from a string is much quieter than when placed on a table.

The effect of the noise sources vary through a hydraulic system. In some cases, when the surfaces of the reservoir resonate with one or more of the driving frequencies, the amplification can be dramatic.

Sources of Noise Generation

As shown by the schematic, the area of greatest noise generating source exists at the rotating members of the system, while noise transmission and amplification is most noticed in the hydraulic reservoir. Also, notice that the rotating members, depending on the type of mounting, can be a prime source of noise transmission. The numbers above and below the schematic represent which component(s) generate or transmit the most noise. The lower the number, the greater noise transmitter generator that component(s) is.

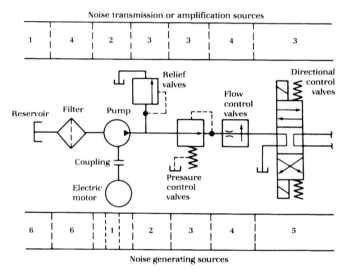

The Electrical Motor Contributes much to the Overall System Noise

Mechanical vibration and noise are generated by the magnetomotive torsional forces between rotor bars and stator slots and by misalignment between end caps and motor frame. These, plus sloppy bearings and dynamic unbalance, can set up structural resonances which can be carried throughout the whole power unit. Any motor with a low number of force pole pairs (4 pairs) is subject to higher vibration and noise levels than a motor containing 6 pairs of force poles.

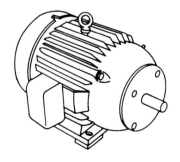

It has also been found that motors with the stator slots filled with an inert plastic have lower noise levels.

Noise from the Motor Cooling Fan

Electric motor cooling fans are a major contributor to noise associated with hydraulic systems. This is especially true if the motor is a TEFC (Totally Enclosed Fan Cooled) motor assembly with metal fan blades and a light sheet metal shroud.

A high speed fan generates loud wind and air stream noises because of its high air turbulence levels. On top of that, the metal blades transmit shaft, bearing and motor noises. Finally, the blades amplify these sounds in addition to the wind sounds. Sometimes a major or minor "siren" effect can be set up if the blades are very close to either the motor or shroud.

Shrouds that are made from lightweight metal and held in place by a few screws, create a drum effect that amplifies both structure-borne and airborne vibrations and noises.

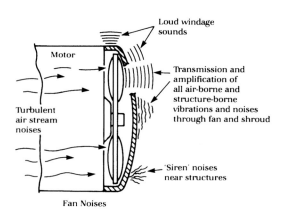

Fan Noises

Noise from the Coupling

The mechanical coupling between the electric motor and pump generates obvious wind noises and there also exists a pronounced mechanical noise in certain types of couplings. These noises are not nearly as important as vibrations and noises resulting from improper pump-motor shafts alignment. Vibrations strong enough to set up destructive resonances can be generated if misalignment exceeds .003" (.076 mm) T.I.R. (Total Indicator Reading).

All rotating equipment will have much higher decibel readings if they are mounted without consideration for their centers of gravity. Translational and rotational forces resulting from unsymmetrical mountings can combine in these cases to generate both structure-borne and airborne noises.

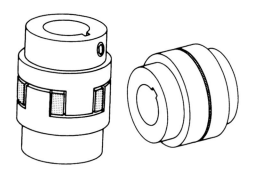

Most Common Causes of Noise

Within the hydraulic part of the system, the most common cause of noise is vibration, contamination and/or cavitation. From these you can trace almost every problem that causes increased noise levels.

Vibration as a problem means, the rotational motion from the electric motor and pump, impact and friction between internal parts, as well as the ripple vibration created by the increasing volume and decreasing volume generated by the pumping action.

When referring to contamination as a probable cause of noise, it means anything foreign in the hydraulic fluid, e.g. dirt, sludge, varnish, metallic wear particles, air, water, tools and cleaning rags.

Some Simple Ways to Reduce Operating Noise

Now that the major whys and hows of industrial power unit noises have been discussed, let us examine some easy, on-the-spot remedies that can be taken to reduce operating noise.

What is about to be discussed are remedies to reduce operating noise by conventional maintenance techniques. However, the best approach to reducing noise is to design the system with that in mind. But, many units are in the field that were designed before OSHA (Occupational Safety and Health Administration) existed and had established noise control criteria.

One of the easiest techniques used in noise reduction is to listen to the power unit. An increase in noise means two types of trouble exists. The first is, damage taking place inside the hydraulic system and/or electric motor. The second is, potential trouble from OSHA, if your machines are emitting more than the allowable noise level permitted for an eight (8) hour work day.

Permissible Noise Exposures

Duration per day, hours	Sound level dBA slow response
8	85
6	92
4	95
3	97
2	100
1 1/2	102
1	105
1/2	110
1/4 or less	115

Problem	Probable Cause	Remedy
Noticeable increase in overall noise level at fittings, pipes, valves and pump or motor (usually accompanied by spongy or jumping operation of actuaors in the system.	A. Aeration	1. Find and repair source air leak at suction side of pump.
	B. Cavitation	1. Find and repair source of restriction at suction side of pump. 2. Collapsed lines.
	C. Foaming oil in reservoir.	1. Check flow velocity in return lines. 2. Analyze hydraulic fluid for proper anti-foam additive. 3. Correct fluid level. 4. Check return line terminating above fluid level.
Pump motor, or valves make loud rattling or clanking noises under load when load when first started up. But, noise disappears shortly.	A. Cold oil is too viscous.	1. Warm up the system with a pre-heater. 2. Run unit under no-load until operating temperature is achieved.
Pump, motor or valves for no apparent reason start making loud rattling or clanking noises. (Accompanied by erratic operation of actuators.	A. Cavitation	1. Find obstruction (restriction) in line and correct it. 2. Clean suction filter.
	Aeration.	1. Find and repair suction leak. 2. Check fluid level in reservoir.
Single loud "pop" or "clank" repeating at regular intervals in pump or hydraulic motor.	A. Aeration	1. Fill reservoir if low on fluid. 2. Tighten all connections.
Increased noise from pump or hydraulic motor. Usually accompanied by sluggish performance.	A. Worn parts	1. Replace or repair pump or motor. 2. Flush system to remove wear particles.
	B. Too thin an oil	1. Check oil temperature. Cooler may need to be added. 2. Check fluid viscosity. If incorrect, flush system and refill with proper viscosity fluid. 3. Check for cavitation or aeration. Remove restrictions and/or repair air leak.
Increased noise from valves, usually chattering sound, sometimes sticking or erratic performance.	A. Worn spools or. orifices.	1. Replace worn parts or entire valve. 2. Flush entire system to remove wear particles and other contaminants.
	B. Electrohydraulic valve cavitation.	1. Check for erratic electronic signals. 2. Replace worn parts or entire valve.

| Loud slam travels through hydraulic system. (Hydraulic shock wave) | A. Sticking part suddenly overcomes the constricting force. | 1. Clean parts to remove varnish and sludge. 2. Check compatability of fluid with system. 3. Flush system thoroughly. |
| | B. Sudden closing of directional valve. | 1. Investigate the installation of an accumulator to absorb shock. |

Reducing the Decibel Level of the Power Unit

Listening to the power unit will help you in locating the problem or cause of the increased noise level. But your goal should be to reduce the decibel and prevent the problem from recurring.

Let us look at the three ways of reducing noise in the power unit. They are:

    Lower generation
    Isolating
    Dampening

Lowering Noise Generation from the Manufacturer

Mentioned previously, the best approach to reducing noise is to design the system or components with that in mind. To lower generation in this manner, the manufacturer should:

1. Select quiet components. In other words, select components which have been specifically designed to have a low decibel output.

2. Use open drip-proof motors wherever possible to eliminate fan noise encountered in TEFC (Totally Enclosed Fan Cooled) motors. Some steps have been taken in this area by motor manufacturers, e.g. plastic fans and oil cooled motors.

3. Design the system to operate efficiently at motor/pump speed of 1200 RPM.

4. Size hydraulic lines so oil velocity is below 15 FPS in pressure lines, and 4 FPS in suction lines, and 8 FPS in return lines. Avoid sharp bends in piping.

5. Size components properly to avoid high heat and noise generation. (If 5 GPM is required, do not use an 8 GPM pump and dump 3 GPM over the relief valve back to tank.)

6. Use stable control valves to eliminate hunting or chattering. For example: a pilot operated relief valve versus a direct acting relief.

7. Specify a good grade of hydraulic fluid with anti-foaming additives to prevent entrainment of air bubbles.

8. Avoid the use of needle valves or low cracking valves wherever possible to help reduce the generation of heat and noise in the system.

9. Design for proper reservoir size which will allow air in the oil to escape. Locate suction lines as far from the return lines as possible with adequate baffling.

10. Supercharge pump, if possible, and in no case exceed maximum inches of mercury inlet vacuum, which is specified by the pump manufacturer.

Isolating the Noise

Once the power unit has been manufactured correctly to reduce the noise level to a minimum dbA level, further noise reduction can be accomplished by isolating the remaining noise generation.

Noise Area	How to Cure or Check	Potential Reduction
		(dbA)
Coupling between pump and motor (high	Shim where necessary, realign to .003" T.I.R. or less	1 - 2
Coupling noise only	Change to type with rubber interfacing	1 - 2
Electric motor vibration	Check for dynamic unbalance.	1 - 2
Electric motor (loud windage noises)	Fill rotor gaps with an inert epoxy. (Time consuming; better to replace motor with one having filled stator gaps.	1 - 2
Electric motor (clatter)	Oil or replace bearings.	1 - 3
Cooling fan (loud windage	Replace metal fan blades with plastic blades or coat metal fan blades with plastic.	1 - 2
Cooling fan (siren noise)	Add spacers for more clearance between blades and motor or blades and cover.	1 - 2
TEFC fan and cover	Tighten loose bolts	1 - 3
Fan cover (windage,) general noises, high vibration	Replace with cast iron cover or coat with heavy mastic cement inside and out.	1 - 2
Pipes and fittings (noise and vibration)	Change to flexible hose with correct psi ratings throughout the system. Insert hose in sharp bend areas and at pump.	3 - 12
Pipes or hoses (rattling noises)	Stabilize with absorbent mounts at frequently spaced intervals.	1 - 3
Mounting plate of pump/ motor (vibration)	Install 1" or heavier pump/motor bed plate; heavy isolaters between plate and reservoir and/or stiffen mount.	2 - 4
Oil reservoir (loud "thrumming")	Add rubber washers under reservoir and under pump/motor mounting plate.	2 - 3

Dampening Noise

The final area that can reduce the noise within the power unit is by dampening or absorbing the noise. Many of the methods used to isolate the noise also dampen the noise at the same time.

The use of hose versus pipe, for example, at the discharge of the pump helps dampen pump ripple and vibration. In conjunction with the use of either hose or pipe, another method of dampening noise transmission and vibration is to tie down the lines at frequent intervals. Two typical mounting brackets are shown, these are very useful if vibration or chatter exist at control or valve panels.

Vibration alone can also be dampened especially at the pump/motor mounting plate and at the reservoir mounting legs by the use of thick resilient rubber washers. And even though the vibration won't be reduced, the resultant noise certainly can be reduced as much as 1-35 dbA by surrounding the reservoir with sound absorbing material.

Hydraulic Acoustic Filter

You can locate in the pump discharge line a device, similar in its operation to a car muffler, a hydraulic acoustic filter (muffler) which effectively reduces pulsations into the system generated by the pumping action of the pump. These components are very costly and their selection and use should only be considered in extremely critical situations.

Power Unit Enclosures - "Dog Houses"

Various enclosures or noise barriers can reduce noise levels from 1 - 35 dbA. Because of the inherent problems of heat buildup, cost for construction and service inconvenience, many maintenance people will only use dog houses as a last resort.

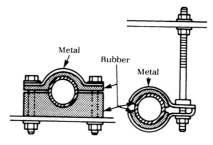

Two typical mount brackets

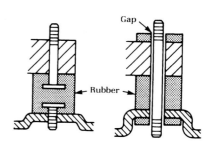

Two types of isolation mounts

Four typical ways of using either a sound barrier or enclosure to reduce the noise level are shown. The barrier method simply separates the power unit from the operator by a vertical wall made of 1" thick plywood and 3" thick acoustical absorbing material, all of which stands at least 6' tall. This method has one drawback; that is, accessibility to all sides of the power unit is impossible without moving the power unit or removal of the barrier

The naturally ventilated dog house completely encloses the power unit. It is constructed from sheet metal and 1" absorbing material. This type of enclosure only reduces the dbA by 1 - 3 dbA because of the open air louvers on both ends for ventilation and the unsealed access doors and floor edge.

The fully sealed dog house reduces noise by 20-25 dbA. However, its construction of heavy steel and 2" damping cement insides, no access doors and no ventilation makes it the less desirable enclosure.

A properly constructed highly effective dog house which can reduce the noise level by 25-35 dbA, has good ventilation, fully sealed access doors and floor edges is ideal, but very costly in its construction and use.

When to use a "Dog House"

Even though dog houses and barriers have their various characteristics and considerations, they can be very useful when:

1. After every other economical noise reduction method has been made, but the dbA level is still above OSHA requirements.

2. Where several noisy machines are very close together and the accumulative effect is above OSHA requirements. Adding dog houses over the noisiest machine(s) can bring the noise level within limits.

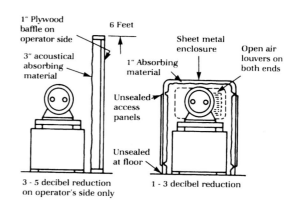

3 - 5 decibel reduction on operator's side only

1 - 3 decibel reduction

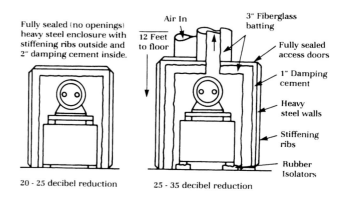

20 - 25 decibel reduction

25 - 35 decibel reduction

Though you can effect a substantial noise reduction with dog houses, this is only noticed at the particular power unit involved. There are other areas to consider to reduce the overall system noise and room noise.

Isolation Room for Power Unit

Pumps, electric motors, and reservoirs are all located inside a separate sound-proof room while the machines that use the hydraulics are located outside the room. Or the reverse arrangements could be used placing the machine(s) inside the special room and the power unit(s) outside the room. A decibel reduction of 70-100 dBA can be achieved.

Other Major Areas of Noise Reduction

The following is a list of other techniques used in reducing both local and ambient noise

Technique	Description	Potential Reduction
		(dbA)
Central hydraulic system (remote)	Pumps, motors and large central reservoir located in nearby isolated room. Accumulators and machine controls located at individual machines in plant.	70 - 100
Component changes and/or additions	Valves, cylinders and hydraulic motors that were noisy when new can be replaced with quieter designed components.	1 - 10 Depending upon how many components replaced.
	Acoustic filters added to the system.	1 - 4 Depending upon type.
Increasing distance	Move noisy machines farther apart to reduce noise level at each operator station.	3 dbA for each time distance is doubled.
Operator enclosure	Shield adjacent operators from noise of a loud machined operation by installing 3-sided enclosure around operator.	5 - 25 dbA at adjacent operator's station.
Ceiling and floor treatment	Sound absorbing materials applied to or suspended from ceiling and and concrete machine foundations with spring and rubber vibration isolation mounts.	15 - 25 dbA ambient reduction
Wall treatment	Sound dampening and/or absorbing materials applied to walls or baffles.	4 - 10 dbA ambient reduction
Personal equipment	Earplugs and earmuffs.	

PUMP MAINTENANCE

The function of a pump in any hydraulic system is to convert the mechanical energy of its prime mover into hydraulic energy. Because of the mechanical operation, rotation and/or reciprocation, the pump creates a partial vacuum at its inlet and in the inlet line. This partial vacuum allows atmospheric pressure to force the fluid in the reservoir through the inlet line and into the pump inlet. The pump carries the fluid to its outlet and delivers it into the hydraulic system.

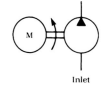

Hydrodynamics and Hydrostatic Pumps

Pumps are classified into two broad categories. The first classification is hydrodynamic or non-positive displacement pumps. Typical examples of this type would be engine water pumps and sump pumps.

Generally they consist of an impeller or propeller and a diffuser housing. They have large clearances between the rotating and stationary members generating a high flow volume but typically low pressures (250-300 psi/17.58-21.1 kg/cm^2). Because of this low pressure generation, they are not commonly used in the fluid power industry, except for transfer of large volumes at low pressure.

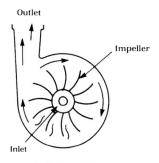

Hydrodynamic

The other classification is hydrostatic or positive displacement. There is a wide variety of positive displacement pumps but we will be concerned with the three most common types: gear, vane and piston.

All three types displace a fixed quantity of fluid per revolution of the pumping members. As a result, pump output flow, minus internal leakage, is relatively a constant. However, consideration must be given to the possible problem of over pressurizing the pump due to excessive flow resistance. The generic term for this positive displacement characteristic is "fixed displacement."

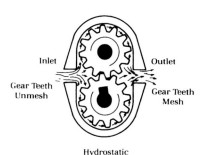

Hydrostatic

Some positive displacement pumps are termed "variable displacement." The output of the pumps, generally vane and piston, can be adjusted and fixed, then the output is considered positive at the adjusted levels, or the output can be automatically controlled to maintain a specific pressure as in the case of a variable volume pressure compensated pump.

Gear Pumps

Gear pumps generate a pumping action by causing the gear set to mesh and unmesh. This gear set could be of either external gear, internal gear, lobe or screw types.

External Gear Pumps

An external gear pump has its gear teeth on the outer circumference of the gear hub. There are basically three types of gears used in external gear pumps -- spur, helical, and herringbone. The spur gear is the easiest to manufacture and is most common. However, it does generate more noise at higher speeds than the others and it also operates at the highest pressure range, 3600-4000 psi (253.2-281.23 kg/cm^2). The helical gear is designed to reduce the noise and provide a smoother operation, but these gears develop excessive end thrust due to the action of the helical gears and can only operate to pressures of 2000 psi (140.7 kg/cm^2). The herringbone gear design eliminates the problem of end thrust, operates quietly and can develop pressures above 750 psi (52.7 kg/cm^2).

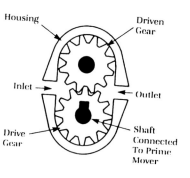

How an External Gear Pump Works

As the drive gear is turned by the prime mover, it meshes with and rotates the driven gear. A positive seal is achieved between the teeth and the housing and between the meshing teeth themselves, as the gears rotate. The action of teeth unmeshing and meshing generates an increasing volume at the inlet and a decreasing volume at the outlet respectively.

At the inlet where gear teeth unmesh, a partial vacuum is formed and fluid is pushed into the pump to fill the void. The fluid is then trapped between the gear teeth and housing, and carried to the other side of the housing. At this point, the gear teeth mesh and force the fluid out into the system.

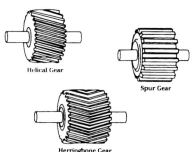

Internal Gear Pump

An internal gear pump consists of one external gear which meshes with the teeth on the inside circumference of a large gear. The most common type is the gerotor pump.

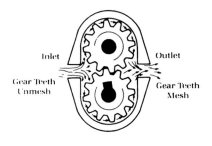

Gerotor Pump

How an Internal Gear Pump Works

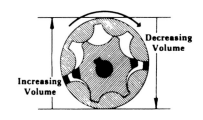

As the inner gear is turned by a prime mover, it drives the larger outer gear. On one side of the pumping mechanism, an increasing volume is formed as gear teeth unmesh. Fluid is carried around to the other side where it is forced out the outlet by the meshing of the gears. The volumetric displacement of this pump is determined by the space generated by the extra tooth in the outer gear.

Lobe Pump

Another gear pump is the lobe rotor. It operates similar to the external gear pump except both lobes are driven by external means and there is no contact between the lobes. This slight clearance allows the pump to run quieter, but it does create a greater amount of pulsation in the flow and its total volumetric displacement is generally higher than the other gear pumps.

Three-Lobe
Pump

Screw pump

The screw pump has three precision ground screws that mesh together inside a housing. The center screw is the drive member, the other two screws are driven members. The pump is quiet and develops pressures in the range of 500 to 3500 psi with volumes up to 123 gpm.

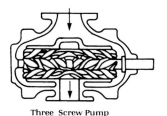

Three Screw Pump

How a Screw Pump Works

As fluid is drawn into the inlet, the flow runs axially through the screws. As the drive screw is driven by a prime mover, the two idler screws carry the fluid toward the outlet by creating a succession of closures or stages.

Vane Pumps

In industrial applications, the vane pump is commonly used. Vane pumps generate a pumping action by causing an increasing volume and decreasing volume at inlet and outlet respectively.

The vane pump can be of fixed or variable displacement, and pressure compensated.

What a Fixed Displacement Vane Consists Of

The pumping mechanism of a typical vane pump is often an integral unit called a cartridge assembly. A cartridge assembly consists of a rotor with vanes and a cam ring sandwiched between two port plates. The port plates of a balanced vane pump have two inlet and two outlet ports.

An advantage of cartridge assembly design is easy pump servicing. After a period of time normal pump wear affects the volumetric output of the pump, the cartridge assembly can easily be removed and replaced with a new cartridge assembly. Also, if for some reason the pump's volume or pressure must be increased or decreased, a cartridge assembly with the same outside dimensions, center spline dimension, and the desired volume can be quickly substituted for the original pumping mechanisms, taking care that the prime mover (driving motor) is capable of driving the new assembly.

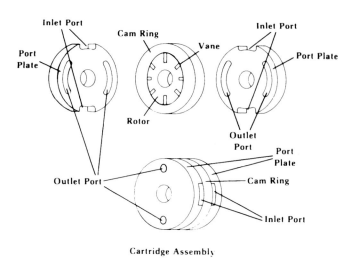

Cartridge Assembly

How a Fixed Displacement Vane Pump Works

The rotor of a vane pump houses the vanes and it is attached to a shaft which is connected to a prime mover. As the rotor is turned, vanes are thrown out by centrifugal force and track along the ring. (The ring is held stationary.) As the vanes make contact, a positive seal is formed between vane tip and ring.

The rotor is positioned in the center of the cam ring in a balanced vane pump. The inside circumference of the ring is oval or "egg" shaped. As the rotor is turned, an increasing and decreasing volume is formed within the ring.

Since there are no ports in the ring, the port plates are used to separate incoming from outgoing fluid. The inlet ports of the port plates are located where the increasing volume is formed. The port plates outlet ports are located where the decreasing volume is generated.

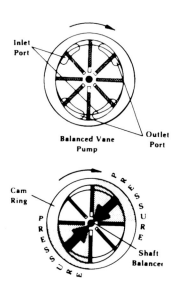

Pressure Compensated Variable Volume Vane Pump Consists Of

The pumping mechanism of a typical pressure compensated variable volume vane pump consists of a rotor with vanes, cam ring, volume stop adjustment screw, thrust bearing and adjustable compensator spring. The variable volume vane pump ring is circular and not oval or "egg" shaped as in the fixed displacement type. Since the cam ring in this type pump must be free to rock from side to side, the pumping mechanism does not come as a cartridge assembly.

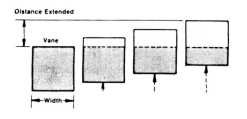

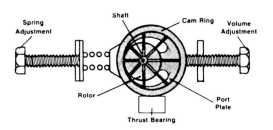

4-4

How Variable Volume Works

Variable volume means that the pump's output can be adjusted manually or automatically to a desired flow rate, which is then held relatively constant.

When the volume adjustment screw is turned completely out, the pressure compensator spring holds the cam ring all the way to one side. This creates an off center relationship between the cam ring and rotor. When the rotor is turned, an increasing volume area and a decreasing volume area are generated. Pumping at maximum volume occurs.

With the volume adjustment screw turned in slightly, the cam ring is moved closer to center in relation to the rotor. An increasing and decreasing volume still exists but not as much flow is being delivered. The difference in volume occurs because the length of vane extension is shortened.

Turning in the volume adjustment screw all the way, centers the cam ring over the rotor. No increasing and decreasing volume areas are generated in this condition. Therefore, no pumping occurs. However, under full flow or no-flow condition, a small amount of internal leakage occurs for lubrication and this leakage is carried away from the pump housing through the case drain port and line.

How Pressure Compensation Works

Pressure compensation means that the pump is capable of maintaining a maximum pressure that is manually or automatically set. An adjustable spring is used to offset the cam ring to the maximum displacement. When the pressure acting on the inner contour of the cam ring is high enough to overcome the force of the spring, the ring centers and except for leakage, pumping ceases. System pressure is, therefore, limited to the setting of the compensator spring.

Spool Compensators

The previous discussion on a vane pump pressure compensator described a simple method of obtaining pressure compensation through spring biasing. Where a higher degree of performance and/or response is required, a spool type compensator is used.

A spool compensated vane pump arrangement consists of a servo and bias piston used to control the cam ring movement. The compensator

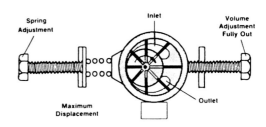

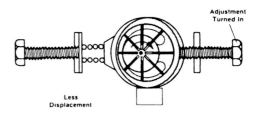

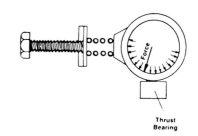

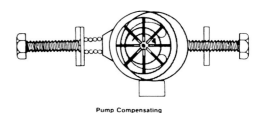

Pump Compensating

valve consists of compensator spool, bias spring and adjustment knob.

How Spool Compensation Works

The rotating group is placed between two pistons (servo and bias pistons). High force developed by the pressure contained within the ring is acting against the thrust screw, so there is little reaction to outlet pressure changes. The bias piston, through internal passages, is acted upon by outlet pressure which is trying to cause the bias piston to move the cam ring to the centered position. Opposite the bias piston is the servo piston which has a larger area, in this case, twice the surface area of the bias piston. Outlet pressure acting on the servo piston develops more force and keeps the cam ring shifted so as to generate flow.

The job of the compensator valve is to control the servo piston pressure thus limiting the total system pressure. The compensator spool itself is a pressure reducing valve connected between pump outlet and the servo piston. The valve is normally passing (open) to allow full pressure to the servo piston, thus holding the cam ring into the full flow position during normal operation.

Outlet pressure is also ported to the blind end of the spool. This creates a force, proportional to outlet pressure, against the spool. If this force exceeds the spring preload, set by the adjustment knob, the spool moves to the right to meter flow from the servo piston to the suction or inlet side or case of the pump. Pressure at the servo piston is reduced allowing the cam ring to be moved toward the centered position by the bias piston. Since we are using outlet pressure to position the spool, it will seek a position which will produce the flow required to maintain the pressure setting of the compensator valve.

If the system pressure drops, the spool bias spring will move the spool porting fluid into the larger area of the servo piston which forces the cam ring over creating a greater increasing and decreasing volume area. We now have outlet pressure limited to a point set with the preload of the spring.

Pilot Operated Pressure Compensation

In some pumps the compensator spool is not just biased by a spring. The spring cavity of the compensator is used as a pressure cavity. The force against the spool is now the spring preload plus the product of any pressure acting on the effective piston area in the spring cavity.

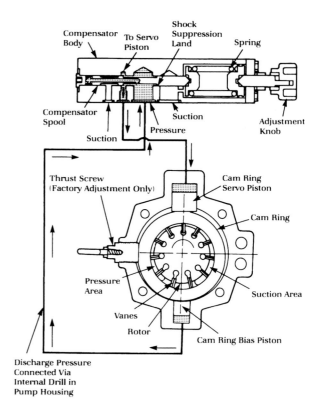

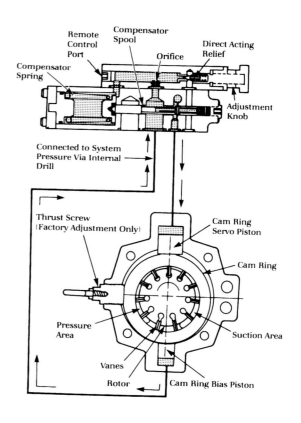

This pressure in the spring cavity may be obtained by supplying pilot oil from the outlet of the pump through an orifice in a pressure limiting valve section. One example of this would be a small direct acting relief dart and spring to limit the cavity pressure.

With this arrangement, the pressure compensator setting is controlled by the spring force upon the dart, the resulting pressure in the spring cavity and the preload of the spool bias spring.

Piston Pumps

Piston pumps generate a pumping action by causing pistons to reciprocate within the piston bores. There are two basic configurations of axial piston pumps.

One configuration is the axial piston, with the pistons parallel to the center line axis of the cylinder block. There are two design types of axial pistons, in-line and bent-axis.

The other configuration is the radial piston which has its pistons arranged radially in the cylinder block.

Piston pumps can be either fixed or variable displacement and with a variety of control options they can be pressure compensated, pressure limiting, load sensing, torque controlling or a combination of these.

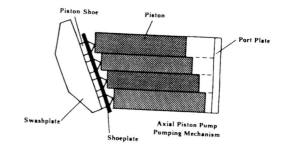

What a Fixed Displacement In-line Piston Pump Consists Of

The pumping mechanism of an in-line piston pump basically consists of a cylinder barrel, piston with shoes, fixed swashplate, shoeplate, shoeplate bias spring (some pumps have individual springs per piston), and port plate.

How an In-line Piston Pump Works

In the example illustrated, a cylinder barrel with one piston bore is fitted with one piston. A swashplate is positioned at an angle. The shoe of the piston rides on the surface of the swashplate.

As the cylinder barrel is rotated, the piston shoe tracks along the surface of the swashplate. Spring and hydraulic pressure keeps the piston in contact with the shoe and swashplate (the swashplate does not rotate). Since the swashplate is at a fixed angle, this results in the piston reciprocating within its bore. During half the revolution, the piston is moved out of the cylinder

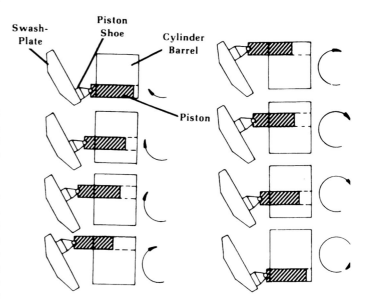

barrel and generates an increasing volume. In the other half of the revolution, the piston is moved into the cylinder barrel and generates a decreasing volume.

In actual practice, the cylinder barrel is fitted with many pistons. The barrel rides against the port plate and the ports are positioned in such a way as to provide proper timing of each individual piston.

What a Fixed Displacement Bent-axis Piston Pump Consists Of

The pumping mechanism of a bent-axis pump consists of a cylinder barrel, pistons, piston linkage, flange, drive shaft and port plate. The center lines of the drive shaft and cylinder barrel are offset most often 23 to 30 degrees angularly.

Because of this large angle, the bent-axis pump is capable of a higher displacement than the in-line piston pump with the same size pistons whose angle of the swashplate is between 17° for pumps rated for 3000 psi (210.92 kg/cm^2) and 20° for pumps rated for 2000 psi (140.61 kg/cm^2).

How a Bent-axis Piston Pump Works

In the bent-axis pump, because of the angular alignment as the shaft is turned, the pistons are pulled out of the barrel during one half of the revolution which generates an increasing volume. During the other half of the revolution, the pistons are pushed into the barrel generating a decreasing volume. As in the in-line type, incoming fluid is separated from discharge fluid by means of a port plate.

Radial Piston Pump

The operation and construction of a radial pump as illustrated consists of a cylinder barrel, pistons with shoes, a rotor with a reaction ring, and a valve block.

The action of a radial piston pump is quite similar to a vane pump. The cylinder barrel, which houses the pistons, is positioned off-center to the ring. As the cylinder barrel is rotated the pistons and shoes track along the ring alternately generating increasing and decreasing volume areas. Fluid enters and is discharged from the pump through the valve block in the center of the pump.

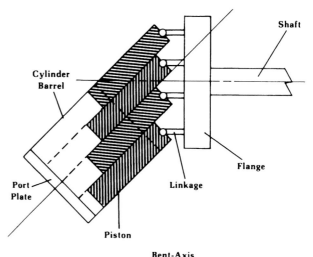

Bent-Axis
Piston Pump

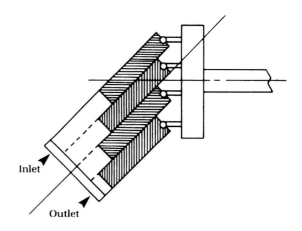

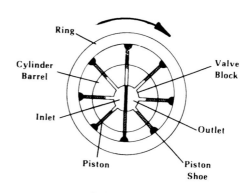

Radial Piston Pump

Variable Volume Piston Pumps

All of the previously discussed fixed displacement piston pumps are also available as variable volume pumps.

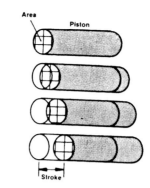

The displacement of a piston pump is determined by the area of the piston and the distance the pistons travel in and out of the cylinder barrel. Since in an in-line, this distance is controlled by swashplate angle, in the bent-axis it is controlled by the angle of the barrel to the shaft; and in the radial it is controlled by the eccentricity of the reaction ring, we only need to change the angle or eccentricity to alter piston stroke and thus pump volume.

How the Variable Volume Adjustment Works

Several means of changing the angle or eccentricity are available. These methods range from a simple handwheel or screw adjustment to sophisticated servo controls. As an example of how the variable volume adjustment works, illustrated is the in-line piston pump. The volume adjustment is a threaded rod which limits the swashplate angle.

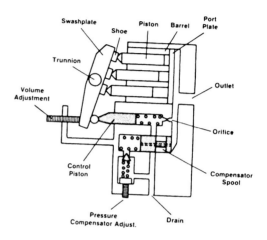

The pump also consists of a swashplate that rocks fore and aft, and a control piston and spring which biases the swashplate to a maximum volume angle.

With the volume adjustment screw backed completely out, the spring plus hydraulic pressure supplied from the outlet port, force the control piston to move the trunnion and swashplate to its maximum angle delivering maximum fluid volume.

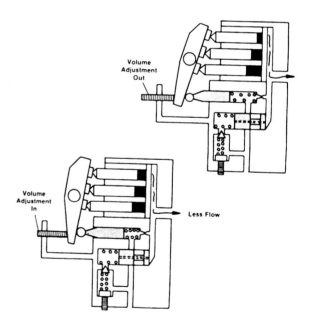

If the threaded rod were screwed in slightly so that the swashplate angle is held to a lesser angle, the pistons would not reciprocate as great a distance in and out of the barrel. The result is less fluid discharging into the system. (The more the volume adjustment screw is turned in, the less is the flow discharging into the system.)

Pressure Compensated Variable Piston Pump

Piston pumps can also be made to pressure compensate. A pressure compensator control of a typical axial piston pump consists of control piston, compensator spool, adjustable pilot valve and bias spring. The adjustable pilot valve and compensator spool and its bias spring are very similar in operation to a pilot operated relief valve.

SAFETY NOTE: A system relief valve set higher, by approximately 200 psi (14.06 kg/cm^2) than the pump compensator, should always be used in conjunction with all types of pressure compensated pumps.

How Pressure Compensation Works

As a pressure compensated pump is operating, pressure acts on the ends of the pistons doing the pumping. With the centerline of the swashplate offset from the centerline of the barrel, the pistons under pressure attempt to push the swashplate to an upright position. This force can be considerable and is counteracted directly by spring and fluid pressure acting on the control piston creating a force balance.

The fluid pressure in the spring cavity of the control piston is developed by discharge pressure of the pump passing through an orifice. At the same time, discharge pressure is sensed through an orifice in the compensator spool. The pressure is allowed to accumulate in the bias spring cavity of the spool and the amount of accumulated pressure is limited by the pilot valve.

When pressure in the bias spring cavity of the compensator spool is sufficiently high enough to overcome the pilot valve spring setting, the compensator spool's spring cavity will vent to case, allowing pressure from the discharge circuit to move the spool left, venting the control piston spring cavity to case.

With discharge pressure slightly above compensator setting, the pressure in the control piston spring cavity is vented fully resulting in a smaller force being generated to offset the force of the pumping pistons acting on the swashplate and trunnion. Thus the swashplate and trunnion are moved towards the zero angle position where the pump is fully compensated or destroked.

When pressure at the pump outlet drops below compensated pressure setting, this drop is sensed at the pilot valve. The spring of the pilot valve forces the valve to seat once again accumulating pressure in the spring cavity of the compensator spool. Now compensator spool spring force and fluid pressure force the compensator spool to return, shutting off the vent passage of the control piston spring cavity.

As pressure increases in the control piston spring cavity, a force imbalance exists between the pumping piston and control piston causing the swashplate and trunnion to move to maximum pumping angle.

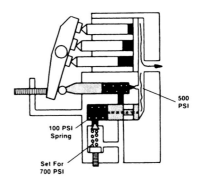

500 PSI
100 PSI Spring
Set For 700 PSI

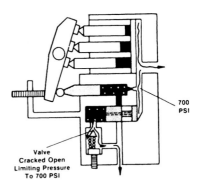

700 PSI
Valve Cracked Open Limiting Pressure To 700 PSI

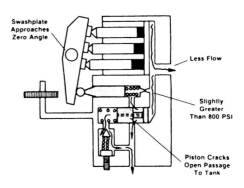

Swashplate Approaches Zero Angle
Less Flow
Slightly Greater Than 800 PSI
Piston Cracks Open Passage To Tank

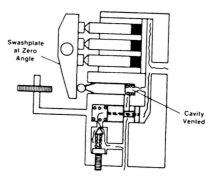

Swashplate at Zero Angle
Cavity Vented

Pump Compensating

Load Sensing

With some variable volume pumps, vane and piston type, it is possible to control flow and still maintain pump pressure very nearly at the pressure required to move the load. This method of compensating is known as load sensing. By installing an external signal line from a point downstream of a system orifice, needle valve, or directional valve used to meter flow, to the pump controls, the pressure sensed at the load is transmitted to the pump controls. The signal is translated by the pump into a flow required to maintain a certain pressure drop between the pump outlet and the sensing point downstream of the restriction.

In industrial application, the principle benefit of load sensing is the energy savings derived by compensating the pump at some pressure close to the pressure required to move a load rather than at full compensated pressure setting.

Another important feature of a load sensing pump is the ability to maintain a set flow regardless of changes in the load and/or input speed. This is especially beneficial in the mobile industry.

How Load Sensing Works

The load sensing option of a typical axial piston pump consists of a servo piston control spool, adjustable pilot valve, orifice plug, and pipe plug.

By placing an orifice (fixed or variable) in the outlet of the pump and connecting a signal line downstream of the orifice, the pressure drop across the orifice will be transmitted back to the pump and act as the governing signal that controls the pump.

Whenever the pressure drop at the system orifice increases, indicating an increase in output flow, the pump attempts to compensate by decreasing the output flow. It does this by sensing the lower pressure on the downstream side of the system orifice through line (c), which is balanced against the pump pressure through passage (d) at the control spool. This pressure in passage (d) moves the control spool to the left venting partially the servo piston spring cavity.

This pressure decrease at the servo piston causes a force imbalance between pumping pistons and servo piston moving the swashplate and trunnion towards the zero, angle until the set pressure drop across the system orifice is maintained and constant flow is again achieved. If the pressure drop across the system orifice decreases, indicating a decrease in output flow, the control spool is forced to the right. This increases pump displacement in an attempt to maintain the predetermined pressure drop and constant flow.

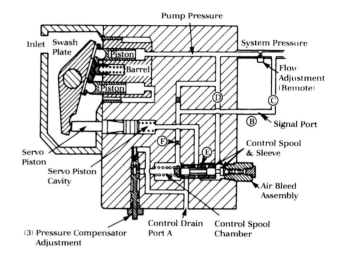

Pump Performance

All manufacturers of pumps have specified the performance characteristics of their pumps. These performance characteristics are illustrated in the form of graphs similar to the one shown.

Though this graph would be depicting efficiencies and data for a pump operating at 1800 rpm on 100 SSU (22 centistokes) viscosity hydraulic fluid, it is still a good tool for checking any deviations from the performance desired. As another check on pump performance, one can listen to a pump while it is operating.

If there is an increase in the level of noise emitted from a pump, it may indicate an increased amount of wear and potential pump failure or air being sucked into the pump inlet. However, you must take into consideration that though pumps generate noise, they are also radiators of noise.

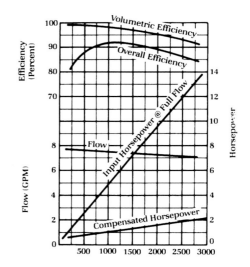

Cavitation

The cause of noise and poor performance of a pump can be related to a problem known as cavitation. Cavitation is the formation and collapse of vapor cavities in the liquid at the pump suction side in gear and vane pumps, but in piston pumps the collapse occurs in the discharge area. Cavitation occurs when there is an excessive amount of vacuum allowing the inlet pressure to fall below the vapor pressure of the fluid.

These cavities that form in the inlet implode in the region of increasing pressure, generally at the first one third area of the inlet. Besides the noise generation, these cavities are harmful to pump life in two ways:

1. They interfere with lubrication.
2. They destroy the metal surfaces in the area of the collapse.

Indication of Cavitation

The most noticeable indication that cavitation is occurring is noise. The rapid and violent collapse of these vapor cavities cause high amplitude vibrations. These vibrations are transmitted throughout the system and sounds like marbles being rattled together in a bag.

Another indicator is a decrease in pump flow rate. This is due to the pumping chambers not completely filling with fluid due to the vapor cavities.

One way to check for cavitation is to install a vacuum gage in the inlet line of the pump. During pump operation, some amount of vacuum should be indicated on the gage. (For exact inlet vacuum limits, consult the pump manufacturer.) However, should an extremely high vacuum gage reading be indicated, check for line restrictions in the pump inlet (suction).

Entrained Air

Another noise generator and cause of poor pump performance is entrained air. Many times, entrained air is present in a system because of a leak in a suction line or a bad pump shaft seal. Both allow air to enter the suction side of the system.

As entrained air bubbles enter the inlet, they have somewhat the same harmful effect on the pump as cavitation. Entrained air will have severe vibration and the noise is distinguished by an erratic popping and banging noise. This noise comes from pockets of air exploding as they are carried around the pump to the discharge port. A lack of lubrication also occurs as well as erosion of the metal surfaces. This erosion and wear will occur at both the inlet and outlet of the pump.

Indication of Entrained Air

As previously stated, noise, a popping, banging, erratic sound, will be the most noticeable indication of entrained air. There is also a significant pressure drop shown by a gage placed in the system. Also you may notice spongy operation of the actuators in the system.

The use of a vacuum gage will indicate entrained air because the gage will indicate a low or zero vacuum. Zero vacuum on a naturally aspirated reservoir can mean air is being drawn into the pump inlet (suction) which causes a pump to aerate.

Troubleshooting Pumps

Thus far, we have discussed the various types of pumps and their respective operations. We've seen that pump efficiency is vital to the overall performance of the hydraulic system and that performance can be hindered by such things as cavitation and entrained air.

Another factor influencing the performance of a pump is the human factor. The person who is responsible for servicing the pump is often the major cause of initial pump failure as well as repeated failures.

The human factor includes: poor maintenance procedures, improper installation, improper oil used, a lack of preventive maintenance knowledge or programs and a lack of training. In an effort to reduce the human factor problem, you must become thoroughly familiar with each hydraulic system you are responsible for. You must be aware of the operating procedures used with the machine.

It is a good idea to record data such as pressures, flow rates, cycle times, etc., when the machine is new or running well after rebuild.

The following sections will point out some of the common pump failures and failure analysis information to aid the maintenance person in troubleshooting the pump.

Hydraulic Fluid

The right type of fluid is essential for efficient pump performance. Some important considerations are:

1. Viscosity - it is a measure of fluid's ability to flow under certain conditions.
2. Additives - consisting of rust and oxidation inhibitors, extreme pressure additives and anti-wear additives.
3. Chemical make-up - petroleum base, soluble oils, water glycol and synthetics. The wrong type fluid can adversely affect pump parts.
4. Brands - never mix different brands of types of fluid unless their compatibility can be guaranteed.

Pump Wear due to Contaminated Fluid

The pump's life expectancy is severely affected by contaminants such as dirt, water, abrasive compounds, varnish and other insoluble contaminants. These contaminants can act as abrasive lapping compounds and/or reduce the lubrication quality of the fluid causing excessive component part wear. This will increase leakage which may drastically decrease pump efficiency adding to the system heat generation.

Typical Abrasive Wear

A swashplate that has failed due to abrasive contaminants in the fluid, will show on the front surface of the swashplate, being extremely and unevenly worn. It is also characterized by a shiny surface and a ridge at the outer circumference. The reverse side of the swashplate shows fatigue cracks in the area where the plate is thinnest. The piston shoes would also be worn and the area of contact between pistons and bore would show scoring.

Effects of Varnish and Sludge

Pump performance is also affected by the build-up of varnish and sludge in the fluid. Varnish and sludge are the result of a chemical reaction between the fluid, air, water, and temperatures above 180° F (82.2° C). This sludge can eventually reduce and plug pump internal passages and create excessive wear.

Varnish coats moving parts leading to excessive internal leakage, poor lubrication and in extreme cases, pump seizures.

Effects of Improper Fluid

There are applications, such as foundries, where extremes in the ambient temperature is experienced. As an example, the temperature can go down to 0° F (-17.8° C) in the winter and up to 100° F (43.3° C) in the summer.

These variations cause the fluid to undergo viscosity changes that may result in pump cavitation, due to high viscosity at low temperatures or excessive internal leakage due to low viscosity at high temperatures. Fluid selection in such situations is critical and may require different types during different seasons. Consult your local oil supplier of hydraulic fluids for assistance in the fluid selection.

The wrong viscosity fluid in a pump can be the cause of many problems such as: parts wear increases due to lack of lubrication, higher operating temperatures due to friction, internal and external leakage increase with thinner fluid, system pressure will be reduced, and overall system performance will degrade. Systems with marginally sized pumps may not perform as required or as expected.

Exceeding Pump Design Limits

It is not a common occurrence, but some pump failures can be attributed to operating the pump above and beyond the specified design limits.

The shaft being twisted, noted by splines being twisted, or the shaft twisted-in-two, is often caused by too high a torque being applied to the shaft.

Excessive operating speeds are another problem that may result in pump cavitation. Essentially industrial pump applications are in an rpm range of 900 to 1200. Mobile applications range between 500 to 3000 rpm.

Troubleshooting Charts

We have seen how fluid contamination and incorrect pump applications can damage the pump. The following charts are designed to help you recognize and remedy some of these problems.

Problem	Probable Cause	Possible Remedy
Pump makes excessive noise.	A. Air leaks in the suction side of pump.	1. Install a vacuum gage in inlet on a naturally aspirated reservoir. 'If indicates zero, air leakage may exist. Replace fitting and/or line. 2. Replace pump shaft seal. 3. Check fluid level. 4. Check pump housing for cracks. 5. Check torque of pump housing bolts.
	B. Aeration of fluid in reservoir.	1. Return lines terminate above fluid level. 2. Check fluid level. Too low causing excessive heat and foam. 3. Check fluid for foam by drawing a sample from reservoir.
	C. Plugged or restricted suction line, suction strainer or filter.	1. Check for proper suction line size. 2. Check for proper filter or strainer size. 3. Remove, clean or replace filter or strainer.
	D. Plugged reservoir filter/ breather filler neck strain.	1. Remove, clean or replace.
	E. Fluid viscosity too high.	1. Drain system and fill with fluid recommended by manufacturer.
	F. Worn or stuck pump parts.	1. Check for burrs or solid contaminants. If burrs, remove, clean and/or replace parts as necessary. If contamination, flush system thoroughly and filter fluid at refill. 2. Pump housing bolts improperly torqued. Loosen and retorque to proper specification.
	G. Improper installation.	1. Check alignment with drive mechanism. 2. Check vane cartridge for "backward" vanes. 3. Check rotation. 4. Check pump rpm. 5. Check relief valve or unloading valve for proper setting.

Problem	Probable Cause	Possible Remedy
Pump fails to deliver fluid.	A. Low fluid level in reservoir.	1. Check fluid level, fill to proper level.
	B. Pump intake restricted. or plugged.	1. Check for proper suction line size. 2. Check for proper filter or strainer size. 3. Remove, clean or replace filter and/or strainer.
	C. Air leak in suction line and/or air lock.	1. Repair leaks. 2. Check pump housing drain port for improper positioning, allowing air to be trapped in housing. 3. Bleed pump inlet.
	D. Pump shaft turning slowly.	1. Check prime mover's RPM. Increase speed to recommended specification. 2. If belt driven (mobile), check belt tension.
	E. Oil viscosity too high or too low.	1. Drain, flush and fill with filtered fluid recommended by pump manufacturer.
	F. Pump shaft or parts broken or worn.	1. Remove and replace broken or worn parts.
	G. Dirt or sludge in the pump.	1. Disassemble & clean pump. 2. Flush system thoroughly and fill with clean, filtered fluid.
	H. Improperly adjusted variable volume adjustment mechanism.	1. Check and set adjustment properly.
	I. Improperly adjusted pressure compensator.	1. Check pressure setting and set properly.
	J. Wrong rotation.	1. Check rotation on pump and prime mover.

...d replace.
...aft for scratches and ...Replace if necessary.

...ghten or replace connections.

...loose or improperly torqued.

1. Disassemble and inspect seals for damage.
2. Retorque to specification. Follow manufacturer's torquing procedure.

Problem	Probable Cause	Possible Remedy
	D. Case drain line too small or restricted. (Shaft seal leaking)	1. Check for proper line and fitting size. 2. Eliminate kinks and bends. 3. Check case pressure against manufacturer's specifications.
	E. Cracked housing overpressurized.	1. Check relief valve pressure setting. 2. Replace pump. 3. Follow pump manufacturer's recommendations for pump start-up procedure.
Pump does not develop pressure.	A. Pump not delivering fluid. B. Vane(s) in vane pump sticking. Piston(s) in piston pump sticking.	1. See corresponding trouble-shooting chart. 1. Disassemble and inspect for burrs and/or varnishing. Replace and/or repair as necessary. 2. Flush system thoroughly and refill with filtered fluid.
	C. System relief valve unloading or compensator malfunction.	1. Check each for broken, worn or stuck parts. If stuck due to contamination, drain, flush and refill system.
Low or erratic pressure.	A. Cold fluid	1. Operate machine to raise temperature of fluid to normal operating temperature. Check pressure again.
	B. Wrong fluid viscosity.	1. Drain and refill system with filtered recommended fluid
	C. Aeration or cavitation.	1. See Excessive Noise trouble-shooting chart.
	D. Excessive pump wear	1. See corresponding troubleshooting chart.
	E. Sticking pump parts	1. Disassemble and repair as necessary. 2. Check for varnish and/or sludge. 3. Clean parts thoroughly, flush and filter entire system.
	F. Pump speed too slow	1. Check rpm and adjust speed; but do not exceed pump specifications.

Problem	Probable Cause	Possible Remedy
Excessive pump wear	A. Abrasive dirt in the hydraulic fluid.	1. Drain and flush system thoroughly. thoroughly. 2. Replace filter elements.
	B. High water content fluid incompatibility.	1. Check manufacturer's recommendation about the use of High Water Content Fluid (HWCF) in the pump.
	C. System pressure exceeding pump rating.	1. Check for possible relief malfunction. 2. Check for other pressure regulator failures.
	D. Oil viscosity too high or too low.	1. Drain, flush and refill system with proper viscosity fluid.
	E. Pump misalignment or belt drive too tight.	1. Check pump alignment with motor and adjust as needed. 2. Check belt tension. 3. Check for thrust loads.
	F. Aeration and cavitation.	1. See Excessive Noise troubleshooting chart. 2. Check parts for the severity of wear and replace if necessary.
Pump parts inside housing broken	A. Seizure due to lack of fluid.	1. Check for cavitation or aeration. 2. Check for too low or too high an oil level. 3. Check viscosity of fluid.
	B. Excessive system pressure above maximum pump rating.	1. Check pressure controls for possible malfunctions. Repair or replace as necessary.
	C. Excessive torquing of housing bolts.	1. Repair or replace parts as necessary. 2. Reassemble following manufacturer's procedures.

PRESSURE CONTROL VALVE MAINTENANCE

In a hydraulic system, pressure control valves are used in several parts of the system for various reasons. These valves come in two forms, normally non-passing or normally passing; and two categories, direct acting and pilot operated.

Normally non-passing valves are relief, unloading, sequence, counterbalance, and braking valves. The size of the valve opening is just large enough to allow sufficient flow to maintain the preset pressure level. When operating, these valves achieve a throttling condition partially and/or fully.

A pressure reducing valve is a normally passing pressure control valve. It restricts and eventually blocks flows to a secondary circuit.

When a pressure control valve is referred to as a "direct acting" valve, it denotes that the spool, poppet, or ball in the valve is held biased by spring pressure on one

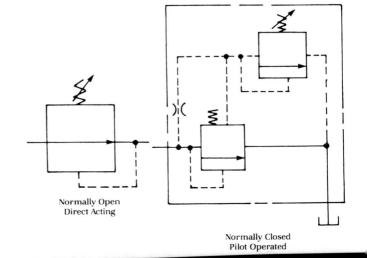

Normally Open
Direct Acting

Normally Closed
Pilot Operated

Relief Valve

Maximum system pressure may be controlled with the use of a relief valve. The valve should be installed as close to the pump as possible for safety and there should be no other valves installed between the relief valve and pump.

In a direct acting relief valve, the primary port is connected to the system pressure while the secondary port is connected to the tank. The adjustment screw predetermines the pressure level at which the moveable member of the valve will move to connect the primary and secondary passages and flow is diverted to tank.

To understand the operation of a pilot operated relief valve, we must present its operation in two phases. The main valve section is one phase of operation and the pilot valve is the second phase. The main valve spool is biased by a light to heavy spring. The stem of the spool plugs the outlet to tank port. System pressure acts on the area under the spool and some fluid is passed through an orifice in the spool skirt to the pilot valve and atop the main spool, thus biasing the main spool with spring and fluid pressure.

The moveable part of the pilot valve is often in the form of a dart. The area of the dart exposed to fluid pressure is relatively small. The spring which biases the dart is rather stiff. The combination of small area and stiff spring means the dart will remain seated until a high pressure is reached.

The pilot valve is a direct acting pressure control valve that handles small flows at high pressures. The adjustment screw determines the fluid pressure that will bias the main spool in combination with the fix rated spring. Once these combination pressures are exceeded by system pressure, the main valve spool is pushed off its seat allowing flow to be diverted to tank.

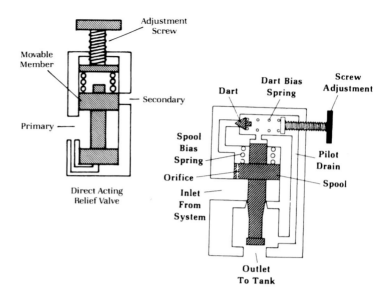

Direct Acting Relief Valve

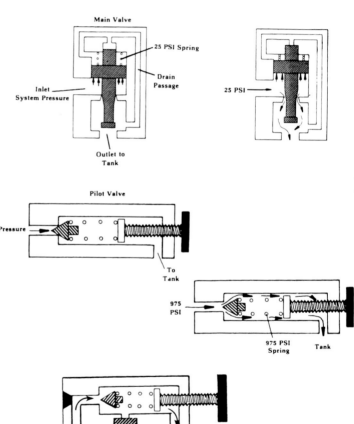

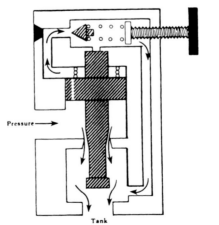

Override Characteristics of Relief Valves

Two two graphs show the functionings of a direct acting relief and a pilot operated relief. The pressure at which either type valve first begins to allow flow through is known as cracking presssure.

With the direct acting relief, note the cracking pressure is significantly low, which allows some flow to be directed to tank and thus reduces the overall efficiency of system flow. But the pilot operated relief valve's cracking pressure typically does not occur until system pressure is approximately 90% of full pressure. This provides a greater system efficiency because less fluid is returned to tank under normal operating conditions.

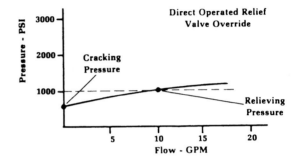

In both types of valves, a pressure increase occurs in relation to flow increase until relief valve setting is achieved. But if for some reason system flow is increased above the flow rating of the valve, a sharp pressure rise (override) occurs in the direct acting relief because of compression of the spool bias spring where as in the pilot operated relief, the rise is minimal because of the slight compression of the light main spool bias spring.

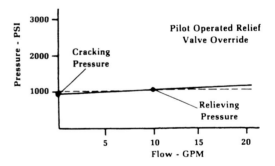

Moreover, the response time of a pilot operated relief valve is often just as fast as a direct acting relief valve with a couple of advantages.

1. System pressure is maintained at a more constant level.

2. There is less chatter due to pressure fluctuation.

Unloading Relief Valve

An unloading valve is a remotely operated normally non-passing pressure control valve which directs flow to tank when pressure in a remote part of a system reaches a predetermined level.

As illustrated in the schematic, a remotely operated unloading valve with its pilot line connected downstream of the check valve, will allow pump flow to return to tank at a minimum pressure when the accumulator is charged to the valve setting.

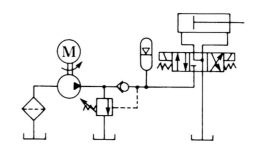

Sequence Valve

A sequence valve causes one operation to occur before another begins. To accomplish this, the main spool is held in a normally closed condition by spring and fluid pressure. The pilot valve adjustment spring determines at which pressure the main spool will shift allowing fluid at the primary port to connect to the secondary port.

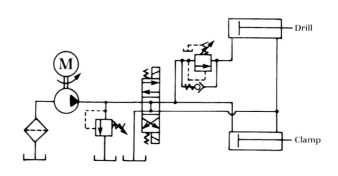

Once the fluid is allowed to flow through the valve, pressure in the primary circuit will remain at least at the pressure setting of the sequence valve.

Counterbalance Valve

Counterbalance valves are usually used to balance or counteract a weight such as a platen of a press. It can also be used to prevent uncontrolled movement such as overcenter cylinder applications or hydraulic motor runaway.

A pilot operated counterbalance valve can be controlled by either internal or remote pilot pressure. As a normally non-passing valve, the spool in the valve will not connect primary and secondary passages until a predetermined pressure, set by the pilot valve, is sensed at the bottom of the spool, and this pressure is greater than the pressure developed by the load which is being counteracted.

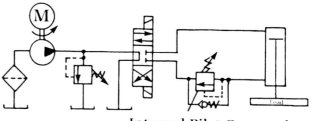

Internal Pilot Operated
Counterbalance Valve

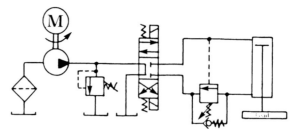

Remote Pilot Operated
Counterbalance Valve

Using a counterbalance valve in a hydraulic motor circuit and positioned at the outlet of the motor will retard the motor rpm. By causing a significant back pressure to be maintained, in order to keep the primary and secondary passages connected, the inertia of a heavy load is absorbed by the pressure differential across the valve, reducing free-wheeling and load runaway.

Brake Valve

A brake valve is a normally non-passing valve with both direct and remote pilots connected simultaneously for its operation. This valve is frequently used with hydraulic motors instead of a counterbalance valve.

A brake valve consists of a valve body with primary and secondary passages, internal and remote pilot passages, spool, piston, bias spring and spring adjuster.

The piston on which the internal pilot pressure acts, has much less cross sectional area than the spool. The area ratio is frequently 8:1.

Assume a brake valve is installed at the motor outlet and set to open at 800 psi (56.25 kg/cm²) of internal pilot pressure. Because of the piston to spool ratio of 8:1, the remote pilot pressure which is connected to the motor inlet, need only reach 100 psi (7.03 kg/cm²) to move the spool, allowing flow from the primary to the secondary passage.

If the load attached to the motor attempted to runaway, pressure drops off in the motor inlet line. The brake valve closes and does not reopen until a back pressure of 800 psi (56.25 kg/cm²) is generated at the motor outlet to slow down the load.

Pressure Reducing Valve

A pressure reducing valve is a normally passing valve that operates by sensing fluid pressure after it has passed through the valve. As pressure downstream equals the setting of the valve, the spool is partially closed causing a restricted flow path. This restriction turns any excess pressure energy ahead of the valve into heat.

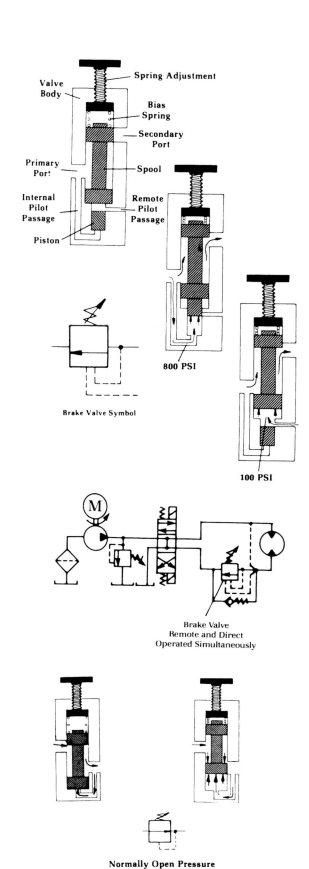

Brake Valve Symbol

800 PSI

100 PSI

Brake Valve
Remote and Direct
Operated Simultaneously

Normally Open Pressure
Control Valve Symbol

If pressure after the valve drops off, the spool will open and allow pressure to build once again.

Solenoid Operated Pressure Control Valves

In addition to pilot operated relief valves, there are solenoid controlled pilot operated relief valves that come equipped with built-in single pressure, bi-pressure, and tri-pressure pilot heads.

The solenoid operated directional control valve mounted on top of the pilot head will either maintain the pressure setting of the main valve, vent the main valve, or direct pilot pressure to remote pilot valves.

Single Pressure with Remote Pilot Adjustment

In the graphic representations of a single pressure solenoid controlled pilot operated relief valve, the directional valve can be single solenoid, or double solenoid equipped. Port "P" of the valve is connected to system pressure; Port "T" is to tank port; Port "A" is to a remote pilot valve; Port "B" is to another remote pilot valve; and Port "B" is plugged.

Operation of the single solenoid operated relief has the main valve being vented when solenoid "A" is de-energized and when solenoid "A" is energized, internal pilot pressure is directed to the remote pilot through port "A."

Operation of the double solenoid operated relief has the system pressure controlled by the main pilot valve when neither solenoid is energized and the "V" port is plugged. Energize solenoid "A" and pilot pressure is directed through Port "A"; energize solenoid "B" and pilot pressure is directed through Port "B" to their respective remote pilots.

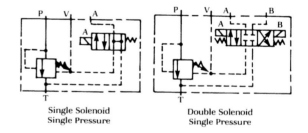

Single Solenoid
Single Pressure

Double Solenoid
Single Pressure

Bi-pressure and Tri-pressure Solenoid Operated Relief Valves

Mounted on top of the bi-pressure pilot is generally a single solenoid operated directional valve. With solenoid de-energized, the system pressure is controlled by pilot head #2. When the solenoid is energized, pilot head #1 controls system pressure.

The tri-pressure relief uses a double solenoid 3-position directional valve. With neither solenoid energized, system pressure is controlled by pilot head #2. Energizing solenoid "A" lets pilot head #3 control system pressure and energizing solenoid "B" lets pilot head #1 control system pressure.

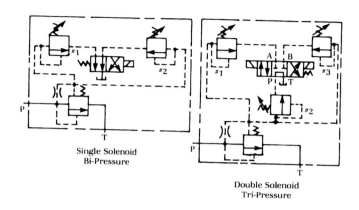

Single Solenoid
Bi-Pressure

Double Solenoid
Tri-Pressure

Remote Pilot Adjustment

When using remote pilot control, the main valve should be set at least 150 psi higher than the remote pilot setting. This helps to prevent hunting and chatter between the two pilots.

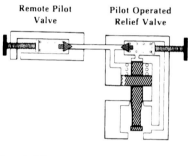

Remote Pilot Valve   Pilot Operated Relief Valve

Generalizations about Pressure Control Valves

Some generalizations can be made about pressure control valves:

1. Pressure control valves, whose secondary ports are pressurized, have external spring cavity drains. (Sequence and pressure reducing valves.)

2. Pressure control valves, whose secondary ports are connected to tank, generally have internal drains. (Relief, unloading, counterbalance and brake valves)

3. To pass reverse flow through a pressure control valve, a check valve, either built-in or separate, is used.

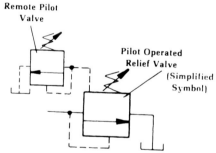

Remote Pilot Valve

Pilot Operated Relief Valve
(Simplified Symbol)

Troubleshooting Pressure Control Valves

Pressure control valves are close tolerance valves. Generally, these valves have very slight if any leakage as long as they are supplied with good, clean hydraulic fluid.

Contamination of the fluid is usually the most common cause of pressure valve failure. Hard dirt such as dust, grinding compound, rust scale, and foundry sand are just a few examples of contaminants that will cause pressure control valves to stick, plug orifices and create abrasive wear between mating parts of the valves. These general problems can all cause inefficient operation or even complete failure of the machine.

Problem	Probable Cause	Possible Remedy
Relief Valve: Low or no pressure	A. Incorrect adjustment	1. Check pressure with gage and readjust.
	B. Contaminants holding valve partially open	1. Disassemble valve and inspect for burrs and other contaminants. 2. Crocus seat and valve spool to remove burrs. 3. Drain and flush the system. Refill with filtered recommended fluid.
	C. Worn or damaged seat, poppet or spool.	1. Replace damaged parts.
	D. Plugged orifice	1. Disassemble and clean.
	E. Broken spring	1. Replace spring if necessary.
	F. Valve spool scored	1. Remove and replace.
	G. Solenoid not working	1. Check electrical voltage supply. 2. Check for loose or broken connection.
System overheating	A. Leaking at valve seat	1. Remove and inspect for contamination and/or burrs. 2. Remove and repair or replace seat. 3. Drain and flush system of contamination. Refill with filtered recommended fluid. 4. Check valve spool for misalignment.
	B. Fluid viscosity too high or too low	1. Drain, flush and refill with filtered recommended fluid.
	C. Working pressure of system same as relief setting	1. Readjust setting to at least 150 psi above working pressure. 2. If working pressure and system pressure cannot be separated by 150 psi setting, consider use of cooler circuit.
Excessive noise or chatter	A. Main pressure setting too close to remote pressure	1. Readjust valves so there is a 150 psi differential between all valves.
	B. Viscosity of fluid too low	1. Drain, flush and refill with recommended filtered fluid.
	C. Worn or faulty seat, spool or poppet	1. Remove and replace.
	D. Wrong spring on spool.	1. Select valve with proper spring rate.
	E. Pressure fluctuation in tank return line	1. Check other return lines for fluctuation. 2. Remove return line. Check for restriction.

Problem	Probable Cause	Possible Remedy
Cannot adjust to low system pressure	A. Improper valve adjustment range	1. Replace valve with correct valve.
	B. Spring cavity drain line or passage plugged	1. Remove and clean valve. 2. Remove, repair and/or replace external drain lines. 3. Check tank return line for obstruction.
Unloading Valve: Pump does not completely unload	A. Low pilot pressure	1. Check for leaks in pilot line and accumulator circuit. 2. Check for collapsed or restricted pilot line.
	B. Pressure setting too high.	1. Readjust pressure setting.
	C. Pump does not build pressure to valve setting	1. Check pump output. Repair or replace pump. 2. Check pump compensator setting if so equipped. Repair, replace or readjust.
	D. Pump designed to maintain a specific "stand by" pressure.	
	E. Valve spool or poppet sticking	1. Remove and clean or replace valve.
Sequence Valve: Secondary circuit does not move or is slow	A. Plugged drain line	1. Check for collapsed line. 2. Remove and replace line.
	B. Relief valve pressure set too close to sequence valve setting	1. Check system pressure. 2. Set system pressure at least 150 psi above sequence valve setting.
	C. Valve pressure setting too high	1. Check and readjust pressure.
	D. Valve spool sticking	1. Remove and clean. 2. Check for burrs. 3. Drain, flush and refill system with filtered recommended fluid.
	E. Valve cover leaking	1. Remove, check and replace gasket as necessary. 2. Check and retorque bolts.
	F. Broken spring(s)	1. Remove and replace.

Problem	Probable Cause	Possible Remedy
Secondary operation occurs too soon	A. Improper pressure	1. Check pressure and readjust.
	B. Excessively heavy load on primary circuit.	1. Check pressure in primary circuit. circuit. 2. Readjust sequence valve pressure setting. 3. Reduce load.
	C. Valve stem and/or seat worn or scored.	1. Remove and replace valve and/or seat. 2. Replace sequence valve.
	D. Contamination on seat seat or in orifices	1. Disassemble and clean.
	E. Orifices too large	1. Refer to service manual or contact manufacturer for proper size. 2. Remove and replace valve spool. 3. Remove and replace sequence valve.
Pressure Reducing Valve: Pressure is erratic	A. Contaminated fluid	1. Drain, flush and refill system.
	B. Fatigue or broken spring	1. Inspect spring tension with tester. 2. Remove and replace spring.
	C. Plugged or restricted drain line	1. Check for crimped or collapsed line. 2. Clean out line. 3. Remove and replace drain line.
	D. Wrong spring	1. If available, check valve spring against dimensional drawing or request information from manufacturer. 2. Replace spring with new spring. 3. Replace reducing valve.
	E. Restricted orifice	1. Remove and clean. 2. Drain, flush and refill system with filtered recommended fluid.
	F. Sticking valve spool	1. Remove and clean. 2. Drain, flush and refill system with filtered recommended fluid. 3. Clean and deburr spool.
	G. Improperly adjusted	1. Check and readjust pressure.
	H. Worn spool, seat or bore	1. Remove spool and replace. 2.Remove seat and replace. 3.Remove and replace valve.

Problem	Probable Cause	Possible Remedy
Brake Valve: Motor continues to run on	A. Sticking spool or piston	1. Disassemble and clean. 2. Drain, flush and refill system with filtered recommended fluid.
	B. Burr on spool or piston	1. Disassemble and remove burrs with crocus cloth. 2. Inspect bore for scoring. Replace valve if necessary.
	C. Improperly adjusted	1. Check pressure setting and readjust.
	D. Worn bore	1. Remove and replace valve.
	E. High inertia load	1. Reduce load.
	F. Bypass check stuck open	1. Inspect for proper installation. 2. Disassemble and inspect for contamination and/or burrs.
Motor does not turn or is slow	A. Collapsed or plugged remote pilot line	1. Inspect line for soft areas or kinks. 2. Remove and flush or replace pilot line.
	B. Improper pressure setting	1. Check pressure setting and readjust.
	C. Valve spool and/or piston sticking	1. Disassemble valve, inspect for burrs and contamination; clean valve. 2. Drain, flush and refill system with filtered recommended fluid.
	D. Low remote pilot pressure	1. Check for leaks and repair. 2. Check system pressure and adjust.
	E. Extremely heavy load	1. Increase system pressure. (Do not exceed motor limts) 2. Lighten load.
	F. Bypass check sticking closed	1. Remove and inspect for contamination. 2. Remove and replace. 3. Inspect for proper installation. 4. Drain, flush and refill system with filtered recommended fluid.
	G. Broken adjustment spring	1. Disassemble and replace spring.

DIRECTIONAL CONTROL VALVE MAINTENANCE

Spool valves are by far the most common type of directional valve used in industrial hydraulics. They generally consist of a body with internal passages that are connected and disconnected by a moveable part. Different configurations are available for various performance and operating characteristics such as on-off operation, reciprocating operation, and proportional operations. The various configurations refer to the number of flow passages within the valve which are termed ways and the number of valve positions, generally 2 or 3, in which the spool is shifted.

A 2-way, 2-position directional valve has two passages that are connected and disconnected by the movement of the spool. In one position, the flow path through the valve is passing. In the other position there is no flow through the valve (non-passing position).

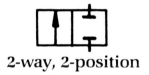

2-way, 2-position

A 3-way, 2-position directional valve has three passages: pump passage, tank passage and actuator passage. With the spool in one position, fluid flows to the actuator. In the other position, the fluid from the same port of the actuator exhaust back to the tank.

3-way, 2-position

A 4-way, 2-position directional valve has four passages: pump passage, tank passage and two actuator passages. The function of this valve is to allow a reversing action of an actuator. In one position, the spool directs pump flow to one actuator passage to pressurize the actuator while fluid from the other actuator passage is directed to the tank passage. In the other position, the flow is reversed through the valve.

4-way, 2-position

3-position Center Conditions

In referring to the various common flow paths available through a directional valve, the flow paths were only considered when the valve was in either of two positions.

Frequently, a 4-way directional valve will come with an intermediate or center position making the valve a 4-way, 3-position valve. The center position of a directional valve is designed to satisfy a need or condition of a system such as, unloading the pump or the system during long idle periods. There are a variety of center conditions available with 4-way directional valves. Some of the more popular center conditions are the open center, closed center, tandem center, and float center.

4-way, 3-position

Open Center Condition

A directional valve with an open center spool has passages P, T, A and B all connected to each other in the center position.

Closed Center Condition

A directional valve with a closed center spool has P, T, A and B passages all blocked in the center position.

Float Center Condition

With a float center spool, the P passage is blocked and A, B and T passages are connected in the center position.

Tandem Center Condition

With a tandem center spool, P and T passages are connected and A and B passages are blocked in the center position.

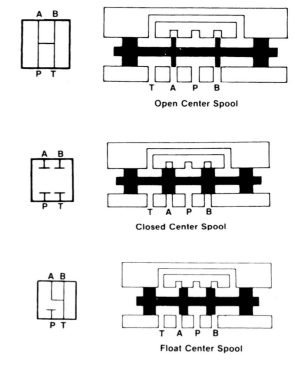

Open Center Spool

Closed Center Spool

Float Center Spool

Tandem Center Spool

Directional Valve Actuators

Directional valve spools can be positioned into 2 or more positions by manual actuation, mechanical actuation, fluid pressure actuation, either air or hydraulic, or electrical actuation.

A two-positioned directional valve uses one type of actuator to shift the directional valve spool to one position and is generally returned to its original (non-actuated) position by means of a spring. Two-position valves of this nature are known as spring offset valves.

Solenoid Actuators

One of the most common ways of operating a directional valve is with an "air gap" or "wet armature" solenoid.

NOTE: The greatest majority of valves manufactured today are of the wet armature design.

A solenoid is an electro-mechanical device which converts electric power into linear mechanical force and motion. Its counterpart in a hydraulic system is a cylinder.

Air Gap Solenoid

Of the two most common types, air gap solenoids are the older design. They are basically an electromagnet made up of a T plunger, wire coil, and C frame. Because of the shape of the plunger and frame around the coil, this is sometimes called a "CT" solenoid.

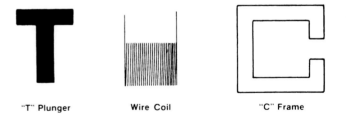

"T" Plunger   Wire Coil   "C" Frame

How an Air Gap Solenoid Works

With an electric current passing through a wire, a magnetic field sets up around the wire. This effect can be seen by sprinkling iron filings on a plastic sheet through which a current-carrying wire is located. The electric current will cause filings to take the shape of its magnetic field.

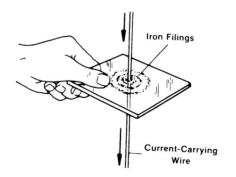

Iron Filings

Current-Carrying Wire

If the wire were coiled in many turns, the magnetic field would be several times stronger generating around the coil and through its center.

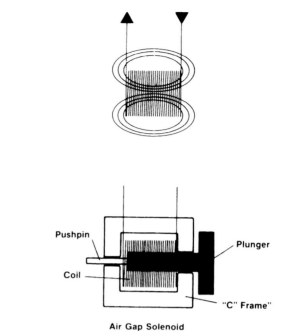

A solenoid depends on this magnetic field to shift a directional valve spool. The more intense the field, the more shifting force will be developed. To intensify a magnetic field, an air gap solenoid is equipped with an iron path, called a C frame, which surrounds the coil. Another iron path, the plunger, is positioned in the center of the coil to concentrate the magnetic field even more; this iron path is moveable.

Air Gap Solenoid

As an air gap solenoid coil receives electric current, the plunger is partially out of the coil. The resultant magnetic field generated from the current attracts the plunger, pulling it in. The directional valve shifts as the plunger hits a pushpin mechanically connected to the valve spool. With the spool shifted, the plunger fully seats within the coil resulting in the magnetic field traveling completely through an iron path. Iron is an excellent magnetic conductor; air is a poor magnetic conductor. Air gap solenoid operation depends on the magnetic field pulling in the plunger, reducing the high resistance air gap within the coil center. As the plunger moves in, the air gap gradually decreases causing solenoid force to become increasingly stronger. Solenoid force is greater with the plunger pulled in than out.

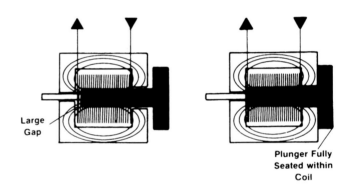

Wet Armature Solenoid

Wet armature solenoid acceptance over air gap designs is due to their increased reliability and elimination of pushpin seals which, in an air gap solenoid, have a tendency to wear and leak or weap on high cycle rate units.

What a Wet Armature Solenoid Consists of

A wet armature solenoid consists of a coil, rectangular frame, pushpin, arma-

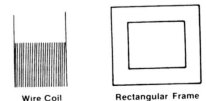

ture (plunger), and tube. The coil is surrounded by the iron frame and both are
typically encapsulated in plastic. In the
encapsulated unit, a hole runs through
the coil center and two sides of the
frame. The tube fits within this bore as it
is screwed into a directional valve body.
Housed within the tube is an armature
which is bathed by system fluid through
the tank passage within the directional
valve. This accounts for the "wet armature" identification.

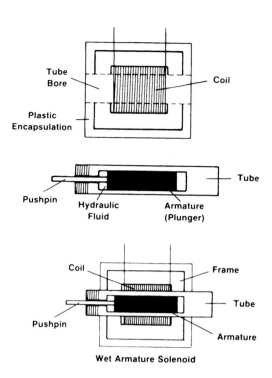

Wet Armature Solenoid

How a Wet Armature Solenoid Works

With an electric current passing through
its windings, a magnetic field sets up
around the coil. This magnetic field is
intensified by the iron path surrounding
the coil and also by the armature in the
coil center.

Iron is an excellent magnetic conductor;
the oil surrounding armature and pushpin is a poor magnetic conductor. Wet
armature solenoid operation depends on
the magnetic field pulling in the armature
reducing the high resistance gap in the
coil center. As the armature moves in,
the gap gradually decreases causing solenoid force to become increasingly
stronger. Solenoid force is greater with
the armature pulled in than out. The goal
of a solenoid design is to have a good
tight magnetic path (iron path) with the
only gaps occurring where you want an
attractive force. With current flowing in
coil, the magnetic force attempts to close
the gap -- if the armature is free, it will
slide to the left to close the gap. Note
that there are now essentially no gaps in
the magnetic path -- good and tight =
lots of force.

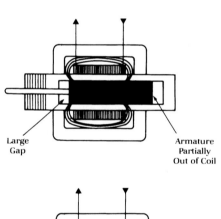

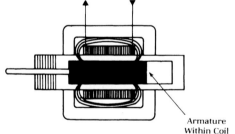

AC Hum

Electrical power with alternating current
(AC) is the usual industrial source of
control power in the United States. Alternating current in the United States
moves from zero to positive, through

zero to negative, and back to zero at the rate of 60 times per second or 60 Hz.

Magnetic field and solenoid force are greatest when current is at maximum positive and negative peak values. As current goes through zero, magnetism and solenoid force decrease. This causes the solenoid load (usually a spring-biased spool) to push out the plunger or armature. When magnetism and force build again, the plunger or armature is pulled back in. This motion results in the solenoid humming, buzzing or chattering and as known as AC hum.

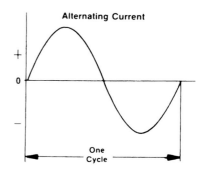

Shading Coils

To minimize AC hum and increase solenoid force, shading coils are used. In an air gap solenoid, shading coils are copper wire loops which are attached to the C frame or the plunger. In a wet armature solenoid, a shading coil is a copper wire ring generally placed at the pushpin end of the tube. As the solenoid operates, current is generated in a shading coil which lags behind the applied current. Now, as the main magnetic field of the coil has its lowest value, the magnetic field of the shading coil is sufficient to hold the plunger or armature in. As a result, AC hum is greatly reduced.

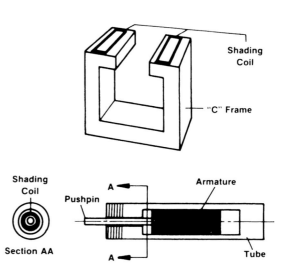

Eddy Currents

AC magnetic fluctuations also cause small stray currents to develop within the solenoid; these are known as eddy currents. Moving in tiny circles within iron magnetic paths, eddy currents consume power, generate heat and reduce solenoid efficiency.

To minimize eddy current effects, the C frame and plunger of air gap solenoids are made up of thin metal sheets which are insulated from one another with an oxide coating. Each metal sheet is known as a lamination. Magnetism can easily flow in its usual path around the coil, but eddy currents cannot readily flow between lamination. Because it is made of

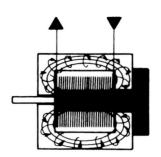

laminated sheets stacked together, a C frame is frequently called a "C stack."

In a wet armature solenoid, eddy current effects are minimized by fabricating the rectangular frame surrounding the coil as laminations. However, this is not the case with the armature. It is impractical from a durability standpoint to fabricate the armature as laminations. In a wet armature solenoid, the armature is one piece but made of special high silicon steel material to minimize eddy currents. By containing eddy currents, heat is reduced and solenoid force is increased.

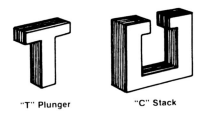

"T" Plunger   "C" Stack

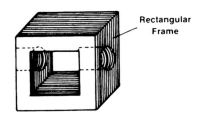

Rectangular Frame

Solenoid Inrush Current

Alternating current in a solenoid coil rises and falls as the applied voltage varies. This results in solenoid force to shift a directional valve spool. It is also the cause of heat generation when maximum current is flowing, which can eventually burn out a solenoid coil. The more current flowing in solenoid windings, the more tendency there is for the solenoid coil to fail.

Unlike positive displacement, industrial hydraulic systems where fluid flow is relatively constant, current flow in the common electrical system is related to the applied voltage and the resistance of the device connected to the power source. The greater the resistance to current flow, the less current will develop and the less heat will be generated. Since heat significantly affects solenoid life, the goal, then, is to achieve sufficient shifting and holding force with as little current as possible. This is accomplished by designing into the coil sufficient AC resistance which is known as impedance.

Impedance is made up of two elements. One element is the result of pure resistance to electron flow of the conductor material; e.g., copper offers less electrical resistance than aluminum (for equal cross sectional area and length). The other element of impedance is the effect generated by the electro-magnetic field surrounding the coil. This field tends to

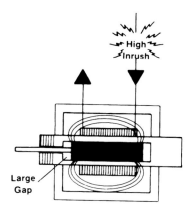

High Inrush

Large Gap

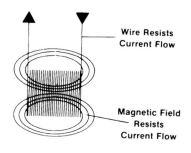

Wire Resists Current Flow

Magnetic Field Resists Current Flow

hold back or restrict current flow into the coil. The stronger the magnetic field becomes, the less current flows in solenoid windings.

As a solenoid is energized, its plunger or armature is partially out of the coil. Magnetic field is not at full strength because of the high magnetic resistance air gap within the coil's center. At this point, resistance to current flow comes primarily from pure resistance to electron flow of the conductor material (coil wire).

Consequently, a high inrush current is experienced in coil windings. This gradually decreases as the plunger or armature moves in, completing ("sealing") the magnetic path. With plunger or armature fully seated, electromagnetic impedance is maximum; alternating current within the solenoid is at its minimum, known as "holding current." Peak inrush current as a solenoid is energized, is several times greater than holding current with plunger or armature fully within the coil. If anything obstructs plunger or armature from fully seating, large amounts of current will rush into the coil generating high temperatures. In a non-encapsulated air gap solenoid, this may cause the plastic bobbin which the coil is wound on, to soften or melt. With encapsulated air gap or wet armature designs, plastic encapsulation bubbles. And in both solenoid types, wire insulation between turns of the coil deteriorates rapidly, shorting out the coil in a minute or two. This is the case as a solenoid attempts to shift a spool which is blocked or stuck.

Continuous Duty Solenoid

A continuous duty solenoid is one that can be held energized indefinitely without overheating. Heat dissipating ability of the solenoid is great enough to dissipate most heat generated by the coil's lower holding current.

"Wet" armature type solenoids of typical industrial hydraulic directional valves are continuous duty solenoids.

Manual Override

Air gap solenoids of industrial hydraulic valves built to "JIC" standards are protected by covers. A small metal pin is located in the end of the cover. The pin is positioned directly in line with the solenoid plunger. As the pin is mechanically pushed into the cover, it contacts the plunger, hitting the valve pushpin shifting the spool. The pin is known as a manual override. The manual override in a wet armature solenoid is located on the end of the tube which houses armature and pushpin.

Manual overrides are used to check movement of a directional valve spool. If a solenoid failed because a spool jammed, spool movement can be checked by pushing in the manual override.

Manual overrides are also used to cycle an actuator without energizing the complete electrical control system. If cylinder operation needs checking or flow controls require adjustment, manual overrides can be used to cycle the actuator.

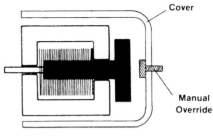

Air Gap Solenoid

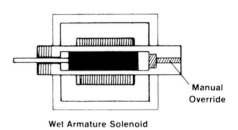

Wet Armature Solenoid

Troubleshooting Solenoids

As an AC solenoid is energized, the coil receives high inrush current that decreases as the plunger closes. If for any reason the plunger cannot close all the way, the inrush current continues until the coil overheats, the insulation burns through and an electrical short occurs between coil turns.

Electrical shorting can be caused by other means, too, but most solenoid burnouts are caused indirectly by high heat -- and directly by the following phemomena.

Solenoid Blockage

A valve spool which has become stuck will block a solenoid plunger or armature from completely closing; this results in a solenoid coil receiving a high inrush cur-

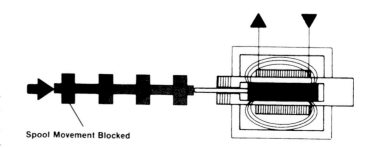

Spool Movement Blocked

rent continuously. The solenoid will be incapable of dissipating the developed heat; and the coil will be burned out.

Although excessive flow through a valve may block a solenoid, mechanical interference of spool movement is the more frequent cause of blockage. Valve spools can become stuck because of contamination like silt, metal chips, coring sand, and Teflon tape or because of burrs which build up between spool and valve body. Oxidized oil particles or varnish can also coat a spool eliminating the clearance between spool and body. Varnish can be removed usually by disassembly and careful washing of affected parts with a suitable fluid.

A solenoid can also become blocked due to a valve mounting surface which is not flat. In this condition, when mounting bolts are tightened, the valve mounting surface may warp slightly, restricting spool movement resulting in coil burnout. Generally, the flatness of a valve mounting surface is required to be within 0.0003 - 0.0005 in.

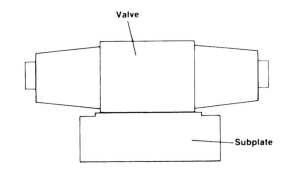

In an air gap solenoid, as a solenoid plunger is drawn into its coil, a wear pattern develops between plunger and C frame. When a solenoid of this type is disassembled, it is recommended that the plunger is replaced in its original position. If not, then different wear patterns on either end of the plunger will not match. The plunger will not fully seat. The solenoid may buzz indicating failure is near.

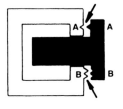

In some cases, a double solenoid valve may have its solenoids energized at the same time. This usually means one plunger or armature fully seats and the other becomes blocked, keeping a solenoid in its open high current position; one solenoid coil burns out as a result. Simultaneous energizing of two solenoids is frequently caused by a failed or faulty component in the electrical control or an incorrect electrical hookup.

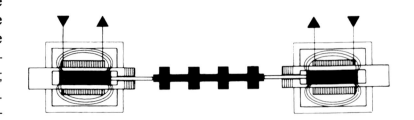

Low Voltage

When line voltage drops below the solenoid's rating (typically below 103 volts for 120V, 60 Hz solenoids), there may not be enough force to drive the plunger home, within the solenoid's designed time factor. The inrush current is held for longer periods of time; without sufficient cooling time between cycles, the coil will burn out.

If someone nearby hears the solenoid buzzing and shuts off the system, the solenoid might be saved from burnout. Otherwise, the high inrush current will continue, closing force will be reduced, increasing heat -- and burnout is inevitable.

This type of coil burnout feeds upon itself; it may take only minutes before actually shorting out. During the last stages, the plunger is held open by the return spring on the spool pushpin. The excessive heat melts the coil bobbin's plastic, which runs into the air gap under the open plunger. After burnout, this plastic hardens in place as the solenoid cools. Thus, if the manual override button on the end of the solenoid is pressed, the hardened plastic will block any movement of the plunger, pushpin, or valve spool, which may mislead the maintenance person into thinking the spool of the valve is blocked.

When checking line voltage, always plug in as close as possible to the solenoid. If checked at a distant point, actual line-loss to the solenoid will not be known. Use an accurately calibrated voltmeter.

Low-voltage problems usually occur during peak periods of the work day when many utility customers are using energy. If low voltage is a continuing problem, install a 24-hour recorder to determine the voltage fluctuations to be expected at the machine. If your available equipment doesn't have one, perhaps your power company can connect such a device to help you overcome your power problem.

Excessive Cycling Rate

When an intermittent-type solenoid is cycled too fast, there is insufficient time between cycles for heat from the excessive inrush current to dissipate. Results: coil burnout with the plunger in open position, and melted nylon under the air gap plunger. (Most hydraulic valve manufacturers use continuous-duty solenoids.)

Other Burnout Causes

Although rare, high line voltage (voltage "spikes") also can burn out a solenoid. In this case, however, there may be no telltale signs of melted plastic as in "air gap" solenoids or bubbled encapsulating materials as in "wet armature" solenoids, since the plunger or armature is locked in the closed position while the excessive holding current overheats and burns out the coil.

A frequent culprit is waterbased, metal-working machine coolant splashing and soaking the lead wires. A buildup of steel chips, or wet or dry, has also been known to conduct a shorting spark.

Another infrequent but equally destructive culprit is the transient spike, or surge, in line voltage. A power surge will cause a spark to jump between the coil and the nearest ground, usually the solenoid "C" stock. This problem is easily identified by a burned out pinhole in the coil wrap.

Certain fire-resistant fluids, such as phosphate esters, can cause shorts between the coil turns. If seals between valve and solenoid wear out and permit these types of fluids to seep into the solenoid, they will dissolve all non-compatible substances, including coil wire insulation and lead-wire insulation. Eventually, an electrical contact will occur between coil turns resulting in localized hot spots and ultimately progressive failure of nearby turns causing a sure failure. Always be sure that the correct seal compound (butyl, neoprene, viton, silicone, etc.) is used, based on the type of fluid being used in the system.

Match Force to Load

Still another problem is subjecting the "air gap" solenoid "C" stack, plunger, and pushpin or the "wet armature" armature and tube to excessive impact force over long periods of operation. When this happens, the copper shading coil becomes worn, deep grooves appear in the "C" stack and plunger laminations of the air gap solenoid and the tube of the wet armature solenoid may show fatigue cracks at the weld areas of the tube.

In fact, a solenoid can literally hammer itself to pieces if excessive impact force, induced by overvoltage, continues. This high force must be absorbed as the plunger or armature hits the "C" stack or tube respectively.

General Tips

When replacing a solenoid, be certain the replacement is of the correct voltage and frequency, and is manufactured for use on that particular valve. Manufacturers of valves use different length pushpins. A short pushpin will not fully extend the spool for proper shifting. A long pin will block the plunger from closing at the end of the stroke, causing coil burnout.

When removing a stuck valve spool, don't hammer it, use a proper solvent to loosen gum, etc. Coat the spool with new oil on reassembly to ease entry, and be sure to insert the right end first if the spool is non-symmetrical in design.

Solenoid Limitations

Solenoid operated directional valves have a few limitations. Where a hydraulic system is used in a wet or explosive environment, ordinary solenoids may not be used unless they are in special large enclosures, such as those specified by such agencies as OSHA, U/L, FM, etc.

Also, where the cycle life of a directional valve must be extremely long, an electrically controlled solenoid valve may not be used. In both cases, the solenoid operated valve may be replaced with a remote air pilot operated valve.

Probably the greatest disadvantage of the typical solenoid is in its size to force ratio. That is to say, that because of their size limitation on directional valves, the force they are capable of developing is limited. Because the force required to shift a directional valve spool is substantial in the larger size valves. The directional valves which use solenoids directly to shift a spool are generally only the 1/4" (3-10 gpm) and 3/8" (10-20 gpm) sizes. The 1/2" (40 gpm), 3/4" (80 gpm), and 1 1/4" (160 gpm) are operated by hydraulic pilot pressure.

Electrohydraulic Directional Flow Control Valves

Over the years an increasing need for higher response, stiffer systems and better flow characteristics have arisen within the industrial hydraulic industry. The use of variable flow electrohydraulic directional flow control valves have met this need. In general, there are two types of variable flow electrohydraulic valves; namely, proportional and servo valves. Which type is used in a particular hydraulic system depends on the sophistication of the design. For example, the level of performance of the proportional valve falls between the previously discussed "bang bang" solenoid operated directional control valve and the more sophisticated servo variable (controllable) valves.

Proportional vs. Servo

There are several areas that distinguish the electrohydraulic proportional valve from a typical electrohydraulic servo valve. These areas are in the overall response of the valve, the spool center condition, the hysteresis, repeatability,

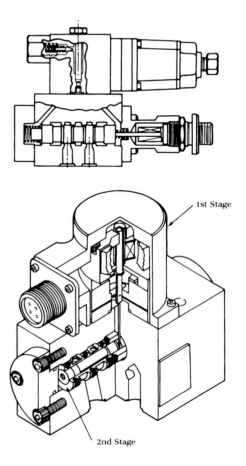

1st Stage

2nd Stage

and threshold of the valve, and the filtration requirements of the valves.

Response

Response is generally designed for proportional valves as the time required for the valve to achieve maximum rated flow due to an electrical step input command signal. When discussing the response of a servo valve, it is generally referred to as frequency response. Frequency is the frequency of the sine wave (AC) electrical input command signal at which the output flow of the valve decreases to 70.7% of its flow at a very low frequency (in the order of 0.1 Hz) with a constant amplitude sine wave electrical input signal.

The response for the typical proportional valve vs. servo valve is 2-10 Hz vs. 10-300 Hz respectively. However, you may find due to proportional valve development, higher response rates are being made available from several manufacturers.

Spool Center Condition

The spool center condition or crossover characteristics of the main spool between the proportional valve and servo valve is quite noticeable.

Servo valves are critically lapped by carefully matching both the width and the position of the spool lands to the metering recesses within the valve body. In other words, the spool and valve body or sleeve are matched to produce a line-line contact often by hand fitting (this adds greatly to their cost).

Proportional valves are designed so that the spools and valve bodies are interchangeable. This typically results in an overlap of about 10-30% of the total spool stroke. The overlap creates a flow condition known as deadband.

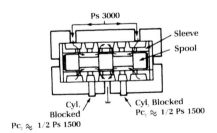

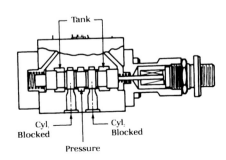

Filtration Requirements

Contamination is the enemy of all hydraulic systems and especially servo valves. Because of their close tolerances, filtration requirements of 3 micrometres are typically specified. Proportional valves are a little more tolerant of contamination and generally require filtration of 10 micrometers.

NOTE: Some proportional valves use small pilot valve heads, thus, requiring additional finer filtration for the flow of fluid being supplied to the pilot head.

Proportional Valve Construction

A typical pilot operated proportional valve consists of the pilot valve, adapter block, wire mesh pilot filter, internal pilot pressure regulator, main spool and body, and LVDT (Linear Variable Differential Transformer).

Another style of proportional valve uses proportional solenoids to operate the main valve spool directly with a positional transducer (LVDT) attached to the end of the valve spool to provide a feedback signal. Still another type of proportional solenoid control pilot operated valve design is used.

How a Direct Operated Proportional Solenoid Directional Valve Works

The main spool is held in the center position by springs. Ports P, T, A and B are all blocked by the lands of the spool.

When the left solenoid is energized, the main spool is moved to the right, proportional to the input electrical command signal directing fluid flow from port P to B.

The positional transducer or LVDT is attached directly to the main spool which measures the precise movement of the spool and feeds this back to the electronics as a voltage signal. In the elec-

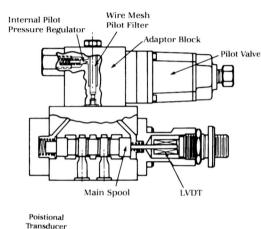

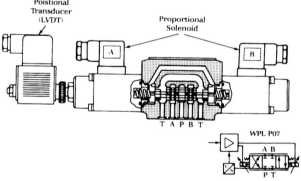

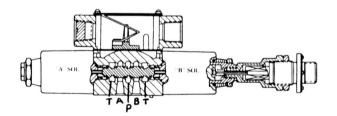

tronics, the feedback signal and the command input signal are compared generating what is called an "error" signal in the electronics. Depending on the sign and magnitude of the "error" signal, the magnitude of the voltage signal to the controlling solenoid will be increased or decreased to achieve desired spool position at which time "error" will equal zero. At the same time, flow from the valve is increased or decreased.

How a Pilot Operated Proportional Solenoid Controlled Directional Valve Works

The main spool is held in the center position by springs. Ports P, A, B and T are blocked by the land areas of the spool. With neither proportional solenoid energized, the pilot spool blocks flow from the pilot supply port.

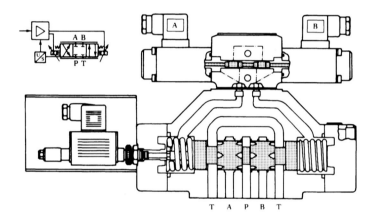

Energizing the left proportional solenoid forces the pilot spool to the right which converts the electrical signal into a pressure signal. Pilot oil is directed to the right spring cavity of the main spool. The metering slots on the main spool open progressively based upon the amount of pressure supplied by the pilot valve.

Attached to the main spool is a positional transducer or LVDT. It functions in the same way as previously discussed for direct operated valves.

A Pressure Differential Proportional Directional Valve

A pressure differential type proportional directional valve is a two stage unit; the pilot valve sometimes called the first stage, and the main slave or second stage valve.

First Stage Pilot Valve Consists Of

The pilot valve basically consists of coil, armature, suspension member, diverter plate, and blade. Some pilot valves incorporate a built-in relief valve and filter to limit pilot pressure and prevent contamination of the orifice(s) in the blade. The pilot valve head is commonly called a torque motor.

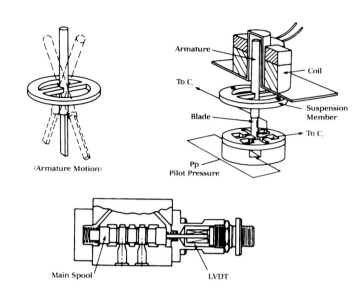

(Armature Motion)

2nd Stage Main Slave Consists Of

The 2nd stage, or main valve, consists of a spool, return springs, and an LVDT. This stage is quite similar to a standard directional valve.

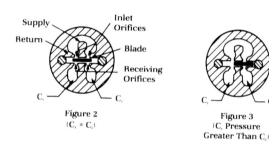

Main Spool   LVDT

How the Pilot Valve Works

Current from the electronics is passed through the coil of the pilot valve. This creates a magnetic field based upon the polarity of the current which is dependent on the polarity of the input command to the electronics. As the current, and therefore the magnetic field, increases, the armature is deflected and pivots on the suspension member and moves the blade.

Pilot pressure is contained in the supply cavity of the diverter plate. This fluid escapes as two jets from the diverter inlet orifices. With the blade centered, the pressure in the receiving orifices is equal and the force to move the spool is zero. If the electrical input signal causes the blade to move to the right, the jet directed to C1 is uninterrupted while C2 is still blocked. C1 will develop a greater pressure than C2 forcing the main spool to shift proportionally.

If the electrical input causes the blade to move to the left, the reverse condition occurs, C2 has a greater pressure than C1.

Figure 2
(C₁ = C₂)

Figure 3
(C₁ Pressure Greater Than C₂)

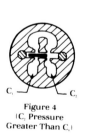

Figure 4
(C₂ Pressure Greater Than C₁)

How the Main Valve Works

As was explained, the valve spool is moved back and forth by the differential pressure generated between C1 and C2.

However, these are not the only forces acting on the spool.

Additional forces due to flow forces, dirt, friction and pressure loading can cause this type of proportional valve main spool to change position. To counteract these problems, an LVDT is attached to the spool which generates an accurate electrical signal back to the electronics to indicate the spool position; this is known as feedback. The LVDT feedback is compared to the input command signal within the electronics. If the two are not equal, the electronics increases or decreases the electrical power to the pilot coil, thereby changing the P from C1 to C2 or vice versa. This repositions the spool where the command input indicates it should be.

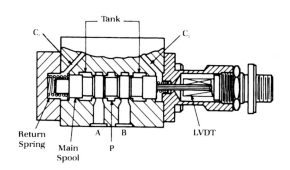

What a Servo Valve Consists Of

A typical servo valve consists of magnet assembly, armature assembly, coil, feedback spring, and main valve spool. The valve is divided into a 1st stage and a 2nd stage.

Types of First Stages

There are three common first stage designs: flapper nozzle, jet pipe and jet diverter. The minimum orifice for a flapper nozzle valve is the 0.0015 clearance between the flapper and the 0.010/0.015 diameter nozzle. A jet pipe valve has a typical nozzle diameter of 0.008/0.010 for the minimum orifice. A jet diverter valve has a minimum orifice diameter of 0.020.

It is not within the context of this textbook to suggest which first stage is best suited for an application; but, it should be noted that the larger the orifice, the more contamination tolerant is the valve.

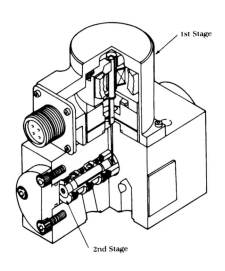

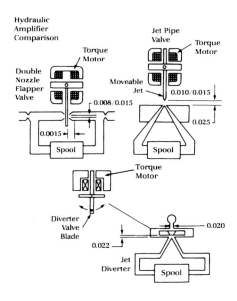

Types of 2nd Stage Spool Designs

The condition or matching of the second stage spool lands at the center position can, and does, vary depending upon the requirements of the system and/or tolerances during manufacturing.

The most common requirement of the system dictates an edge condition of the spool lands and ports in the valve body. The spool lands and ports can be "line-to-line," "underlapped," or "overlapped." Each one of these creates unique flow characteristics within the valve.

Line-to-Line Condition

This line-to-line condition results in an ideal flow gain plot where the output flow to the cylinder ports is zero with the spool in the center position and increases immediately with spool travel.

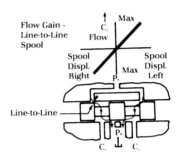

Underlapped Condition

An underlapped condition has more clearance between the spool land edges and metering notches or ports in the spool sleeve or valve body. This results in a higher leakage flow in the center spool position. Note that with this condition, the spool must travel through the underlap before flow begins to the cylinder port.

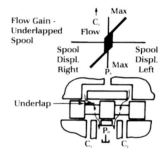

Overlapped Condition

An overlapped condition will reduce leakage flow to a minimum, but again, no cylinder port flow will occur until the spool has traveled through the overlap. It should be noted that this configuration creates what is known as "deadband" in the valve operation. Deadband is a zone of valve movement in either dirction from center where no actuator (cylinder or motor) response to input signal occurs.

NOTE: This condition also occurs in proportional valves previously discussed.

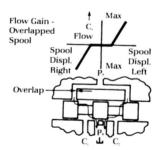

How a Servo Valve Works

A typical first stage section operation was explained in the proportional valve operating discussion and it is the same for servo valves.

The differential pressure created by the first stage is applied across the ends of the second stage spool and will cause it to move. In order to locate the spool into a position that is proportional to the electrical input command, a feedback spring connects the first stage armature and second stage spool together.

This spring can be considered as a cantilever beam that is sized to provide a linear resisting force that is equal to the torque motor force for every spool position. When there is no electrical command, the diverter blade/armature assembly, the feedback spring, and the center position of the spool have a center line relationship.

Applying an input command signal to the torque motor causes the diverter blade/armature assembly to move, generating a differential pressure between C1 and C2. Again, the spool is moved and at the same time deflecting the feedback spring developing a torque in opposition to the motor torque. When the spool has moved to the point where these two torques are equal, the diverter blade/armature assembly, the feedback spring and the spool are essentially re-centered and spool movement stops at this new position related to input command signal. As the input command signal is reduced to zero, the torques go to zero and the spool returns to its center position.

Troubleshooting Directional Control Valves

Basically, all of the directional control valves operate in similar manners; that is, they are solenoid operated, manually operated, pilot operated, or a combination of these methods. Therefore, problems that occur in their operations are quite similar.

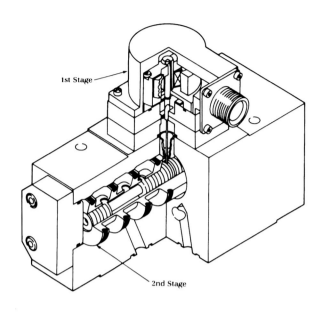

1st Stage

2nd Stage

Figure 3
(C₁ Pressure
Greater Than C₂)

Figure 4
(C₂ Pressure
Greater Than C₁)

Problem	Probable Cause	Possible Remedy
Valve spool will not return to center	A. Pilot drain plugged	1. Check internal or external drain ports for blockage. 2. Check external drain line for kinks or collapsed line.
	B. Pilot valve stuck in one position	1. Check for solenoid burnout or seizure. 2. Remove and clean pilot valve spool. 3. Check pilot valve springs for proper tension.
	C. Return spring(s) weak or broken.	1. Remove and replace.
	D. Torque motor feedback spring broken (servo valve)	1. Remove and replace.
	E. Contamination and/or burr on spool.	1. Remove, disassemble, and clean valve. 2. Remove burr with crocus cloth or stone. 3. Replace valve body or entire valve. 4. Clean and flush entire system.
Valve spool does not shift	A. Solenoid(s) failure	1. See Solenoid Troubleshooting section.
	B. Low or no pilot pressure	1. Check the pilot pressure source. 2. Check and clean pilot orifices. 3. Check for collapsed external pilot supply line.
	C. Pilot valve spool sticking	1. Remove and clean pilot valve spool. 2. Check for improper valve torque. 3. Check for and remove burrs.
	D. Torque motor failure	1. Check for improper voltage. 2. Electronics failure, replace card.
	E. Valve body distortion	1. Loosen mounting bolts and retorque. 2. Loosen rigid piping to remove strain.
	F. Valve spool sticking	1. Remove and clean. 2. Remove burr(s) on spool and/or in housing. 3. Clean and flush system.
	G. Contamination	1. Clean and flush system thoroughly.

Problem	Probable Cause	Possible Remedy
Valve spool slow in shifting	A. Too high an oil viscosity	1. Change proper oil viscosity. 2. Use tank pre-heater. 3. Warm oil by dumping over relief valve.
	B. Restricted pilot drain	1. Check internal drain for restriction and clean. 2. Check external drain for collapsed or restricted line. 3. Check for high return-to-tank backpressure.
	C. Pilot pressure too low	1. Check pilot source pressure. 2. Switch from internal to external pilot supply.
	D. Pilot valve spool not shifting completely	1. Check solenoid voltage. 2. Check solenoid(s) according to Solenoid Troubleshooting section. 3. Remove, clean and/or deburr spool.
	E. Torque motor faulty	1. Check signal voltage. 2. Electronic failure, replace card.
	F. Valve body distorted	1. Loosen mounting bolts and retorque. 2. Realign piping to remove strain.
	G. Contamination	1. Clean and flush system thoroughly.
Incorrect actuator response when valve is shifted	A. Improperly installed electrical connections	1. Check wiring diagram and rewire.
	B. Improperly installed hose or pipe connections	1. Check piping diagram and replumb.
	C. Improperly assembled valve	1. Check assembly procedure and rebuild.
	D. Spool end for end	1. Remove spool, reverse and re-install.

One final comment about solenoids, servos, and valves. These items are designed to do specific jobs under specific operating conditions of voltage, load, heat, pressure, oil, etc. If these conditions are efficiently maintained, checked and controlled, the components and entire system will have significant service life. It's the no-maintenance system that is costly in downtime and troubleshooting hours.

FLOW CONTROL VALVE & CHECK VALVE MAINTENANCE

The function of a flow control valve is to control the rate of fluid flow in its leg of a circuit. It performs its function by being a higher than normal restriction for the system.

This higher than normal restriction is a relatively small opening in the flow path known as an orifice. The simplest form of this orifice can be a pipe plug with a drilled hole in its center placed in a component's flow porting.

These types of orifices can function very well within limits. Because they will restrict flow in either direction, it is important that they be placed only in specific locations and then identified. Identifying their location can be as simple as noting them on the schematic or labeling them on the machine.

Needle Valve

Many times an adjustable orifice is more desirable than a fixed orifice because of its degree of flexibility.

The most frequently used adjustable orifice in an industrial hydraulic system is a needle valve.

The size of the opening is changed by the positioning of the cone in relation to its seat. As flow is passed through the valve, it is forced to make 90° turns within the valve. This flow condition causes a lot of turbulence in the fluid which generates a lot of heat. The heat is a product of the flow characteristic and the pressure losses through the valve.

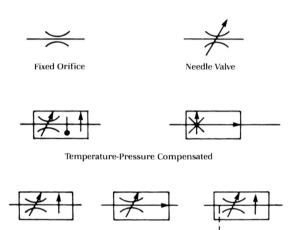

Fixed Orifice   Needle Valve

Temperature-Pressure Compensated

Pressure Compensated

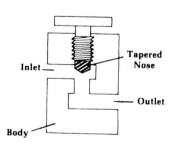

The positioning of the cone (needle) in relation to its seat is one of the factors which determines the amount of flow rate through the valve. However, flow rate through a needle valve can be affected by the pressure differential across the orifice and/or the temperature of the fluid.

Pressure Differential

Pressure in a hydraulic system is potential energy, the greater the pressure entering the needle valve and the lower the pressure exiting the needle valve, the greater the flow rate through the needle valve. This pressure difference is known as pressure differential across the orifice.

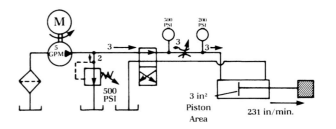

Pressure Compensated Flow Control Valves

Any change in pressure ahead or after an orifice affects flow through the orifice resulting in a change in actuator speed. This pressure change must be compensated for, before an orifice can precisely meter fluid flow.

A pressure compensated flow control valve provides a specific pressure drop across the orifice. Pressure compensated flow control valves are classified as either restrictor or bypass types.

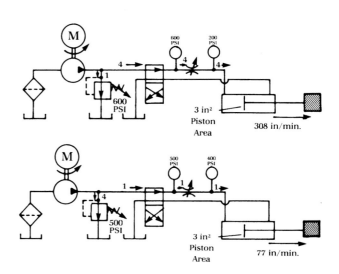

Restrictor Type Pressure Compensated Flow Control Valve

A typical restrictor type pressure compensated flow control valve consists of a valve body, a needle valve, a compensator spool, and a bias spring.

How a Restrictor Type Pressure Compensated Flow Control Valve Works

With the needle valve orifice adjusted for something less than pump flow, pressure ahead of the needle valve wants to climb

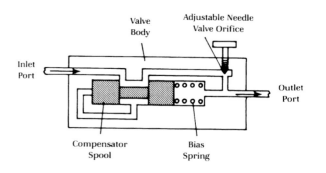

to the relief valve setting. When the pressure attempts to rise above the value of the compensator spool bias spring, the spool moves and restricts flow to the needle valve.

As the fluid passes over this restriction, all of the pressure energy in excess of the value of the bias spring is turned into heat. This means that regardless of what the pressure is at the flow control inlet, the pressure ahead of the needle valve will always be equal to the bias spring value.

In addition to controlling the pressure ahead of the orifice, any fluctuation in pressure after the orifice must also be compensated for. In other words, a constant pressure differential across the orifice must be maintained. To accomplish this, a pilot passage which senses pressure downstream of the orifice is directed into the bias spring chamber. Now two pressures bias the compensator spool towards the inlet.

As an example of the valve's operation, let us assume the bias spring has a value of 100 psi (7.03 kg/cm²), fluid pressure ahead of the orifice would be limited to 100 psi (7.03 kg/cm²) above the pressure after the orifice.

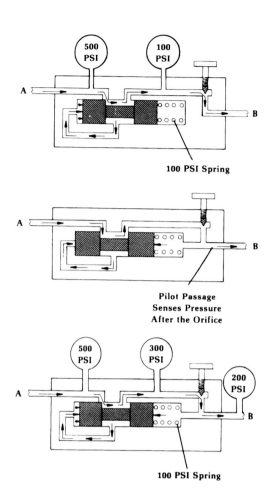

100 PSI Spring

Pilot Passage
Senses Pressure
After the Orifice

100 PSI Spring

A Bypass Type Pressure Compensated Flow Control Valve

A bypass type pressure compensated flow control valve consists of a valve body with inlet, outlet and tank ports; a needle valve; a compensator spool; and a bias spring.

How a Bypass Type Pressure Compensated Flow Control Valve Works

The operation of the bypass type pressure compensated flow control valve is the same except for the bypass function.

Instead of restricting the flow to the needle valve, the bypass type valve estab-

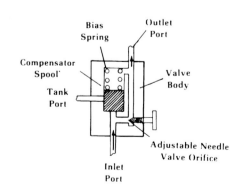

lishes a constant pressure ahead of the needle valve by uncovering a passage to tank or to a secondary circuit (flow divider function). Thus limiting the pressure ahead of the needle valve to a value equal to the pressure of the bias spring plus the pressure downstream of the orifice.

One advantage of this type valve over the restrictor type, is in the reduction of heat generation within the system. Instead of returning the excess fluid to tank via the system relief valve, where a high pressure drop exists, the excess fluid is returned to tank via the bypass tank port at a lower pressure drop.

Temperature Affects Flow

So far, it has been shown that flow through an orifice is affected by the size of the orifice and the pressure differential across the orifice. Flow through an orifice is also affected by temperature which changes a liquid's viscosity (SSU).

As the chart shows the SSU of some typical fluids changes as temperature of the fluid increases. In other words, as the fluid temperature increases, the fluid thins out and is able to increase its flow rate through the orifice. If precise actuator speed is necessary, a change in fluid temperature must be compensated for.

Temperature Compensation with a Sharp Edge Orifice

Laboratory experiments have shown when liquid passes through a properly shaped orifice with a sharp edge, rate of flow is not affected by temperature within a small temperature range of 80-140° F (26.7-60° C). The manner in which liquid is sheared, while moving across a sharp edge, is of such a character that it actually cancels out or neutralizes the effect of a fluid's change in viscosity. The reason this occurs is not clearly understood, but its effect results in very accurate control.

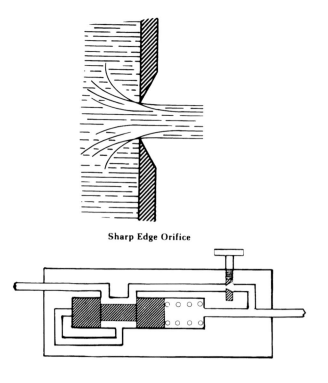

Sharp Edge Orifice

Temperature-Pressure Compensated Flow Control Valve

Combining the features of temperature and pressure compensation within one valve gives you a very accurate control device.

Lunge Control

One condition that may be found in the operation of either a pressure compensated or temperature pressure compensated flow control valve is a jump or lunge condition.

When flow is not being metered through the valve, the restrictor type compensator spool is shifted to a fully open position by the bias spring. When it comes time for the valve to operate, the orifice is directly subjected to the pump's pressurized full flow, before the compensator can react. This causes a burst of fluid to be pushed through the orifice and results in a jump or lunge at the actuator.

To avoid this situation, the valve can be equipped with a lunger control. This is a screw adjustment which pre-positions the compensator spool so that when flow occurs through the valve, the spool compensates immediately.

Setting the Lunge Control Adjustment

The lunge control adjustment is actually effective for only one flow setting of the orifice. Because of this, each time the orifice is adjusted, the lunge control must also be adjusted.

Readjusting the lunge control each time may be very inconvenient; therefore, adjust the lunge control for the maximum operating speed of the actuator.

1. Back lunge control adjustment screw out until you do not feel any tension.

2. With actuator under full load and fluid at normal operating temperature, set

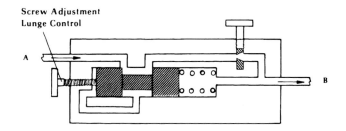

normal operating temperature, the desired orifice opening to obtain desired actuator speed.

3. While the actuator is operating at full load during the speed control mode, turn in the lunger control until contact is made.

4. Back off the lunge control adjustment until free of the spool (no resistance is felt).

5. Turn lunge control adjustment out one complete turn.

6. Recycle the system and check condition of lunge. It should be almost completely eliminated.

Acceleration and Deceleration Flow Control Valves

Many hydraulic applications require a controlled speed as the actuator is being removed from a work piece and then must speed up to get into position for the next cycle (acceleration). Or the opposite cycle must occur where the actuator must approach the work piece at full speed but slow down (deceleration) at the point of work.

To accomplish these two different flow requirements, a deceleration valve is employed. The basic type available is normally passing. Deceleration valves are cam operated orifices with a tapered spool. As the cam depresses the plunger on a normally passing valve, the flow through the valve is gradually decreased until it is completely shut off.

If a small controlled flow is desired when the valve is in a fully closed condition, the valve can be equipped with an adjustable orifice.

Pilot Operated Flow Control Valves

Some manufacturers provide flow controls that are pilot operated. These

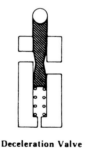

Deceleration Valve

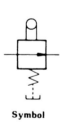

Symbol

valves have tapered spools that are normally open or closed depending upon whether the spool is spring biased or double pilot operated.

In the case of a spring biased flow control, the spool is held closed. When pilot pressure is applied to the large piston, the valve will open. A minimum pilot pressure is required, based on spring value, to crack open the valve. As pilot pressure is increased, the valve opening increases allowing more flow through the valve.

Double pilot operated valves feature a pilot port on each end of the body. Since no springs are used, pilot pressure must always be maintained to hold the valve open or closed.

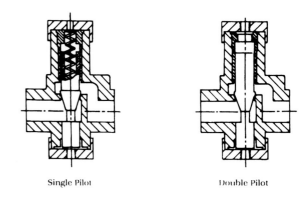

Single Pilot   Double Pilot

Reverse Flow Through a Flow Control Valve

Flow into or out of an actuator is usually controlled in one direction only. To bypass a flow control valve, free flow around the valve, a check valve is used.

The check valve is held closed by high pressure and bias spring pressure during the controlled flow mode. The check can be built-in or a separate component.

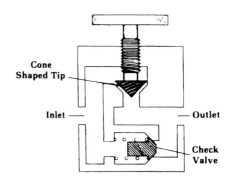

Check Valves

A check valve is actually classified as a directional control valve. It allows flow in only one direction and blocks flow in the opposite direction.

Various types of check valves for various applications are available. Different types are simple checks, pilot operated checks and adjustable checks.

Simple and 90° Checks

A simple check valve and a 90° check valve consist of a valve body with inlet and outlet ports; a moveable member most often a ball or poppet; and bias spring.

Spring Loaded

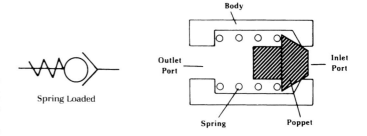

7-7

When pressure at the check inlet is high enough to overcome the spring, the poppet is pushed off its seat allowing free flow through the valve.

When fluid attempts to enter at the outlet, the poppet is pushed upon its seat. Flow is blocked.

Pilot Operated Check

A pilot operated check valve is used quite frequently in applications where the load must be held for a period of time without drift.

A pilot operated check consists of valve body with inlet and outlet ports and a drain port; a poppet with a bias spring; a plunger and plunger piston with bias spring.

This type valve allows free flow from its inlet port to its outlet port just as a simple check valve. And when flow is attempted from the outlet to the inlet the poppet is forced onto its seat just as a simple check.

The main difference is when reverse flow is needed through the valve, enough pilot pressure at the plunger piston moves the plunger piston and plunger, unseating the poppet.

Double Pilot Operated Check Valve

Some applications require the load to be locked in place. A sandwich style double pilot operated check valve can accomplish this function.

This valve mounts between the directional valve and the subplate. A check is built into each cylinder port passage. As flow from the directional valve enters port "B," it passes the check and at the same time, pressure acts on the plunger piston moving it to the left, unseating the check in port "A," thus permitting reverse flow through this passage. Shifting the directional valve will cause the same

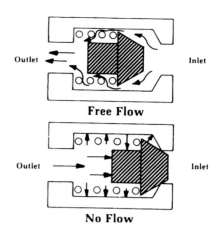

Free Flow

No Flow

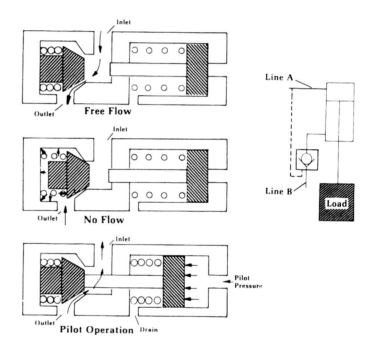

Free Flow

No Flow

Pilot Operation

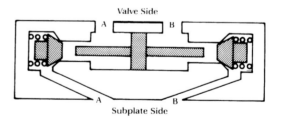

Valve Side

Subplate Side

functions to occur in the opposite direction.

Adjustable Check Valves

Adjustable check valves consist of a valve body with inlet and outlet port at 90° , a poppet with bias spring and an adjustment screw.

The adjustable knob allows you to select a cracking pressure in applications where loads may vary.

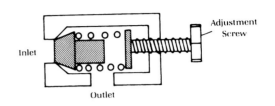

Troubleshooting Flow Control and Check Valves

The simple needle valve discussed can best perform its function within a circuit when the load, pressure and temperature of the fluid remains constant. We have seen that when these criteria cannot be maintained, special flow controls, pressure compensated or temperature-pressure compensated flow control valves are used. The following problems are general areas of valve malfunctions within the system.

NOTE: If any disassembly of components is required, component manufacturer's approval must be obtained prior to disassembly.

Problem	Probable Cause	Possible Remedy
Variations in Flow	A. Valve compensator spool binding	1. Disassemble and clean. Flush system. 2. Check for burrs on spool and body.
	B. Insufficient pressure differential across the orifice	1. Increase system pressure. 2. Decrease system load.
	C. Fluid viscosity too high or too low (needle valve and pressure compensated valve	1. Warm oil to normal operating temperature. 2. Change fluid to recommended SSU. 3. Change valve to temperature pressure compensated valve.
	D. Leakage at or inside actuator	1. Repair external or internal leakage of actuator.
	E. Erratic pilot pressure	1. Check cause of pilot pressure drops.
Improper flow rate	A. Needle valve adjustment incorrect	1. Readjust needle valve.
	B. Additional line restriction	1. Check for collapsed or kinked lines. 2. Check for proper tube fitting and hose size.
	C. Restrictions in valve passages or orifice area	1. Disassemble and clean. 2. Flush system.
	D. Compensator spool sticking	1. Disassemble and clean. 2. Check for burrs on spool and body. 3. Check for broken spring. Replace. 4. Flush system.
	E. Fluid too hot	1. Reduce gpm's over relief valve. 2. Change to bypass type flow control, if possible. 3. Check fluid, SSU. 4. Change to larger capacity flow
	G. Low pilot pressure	1. Increase pilot pressure. 2. Check for collapsed or leaking pilot line.

Problem	Probable Cause	Possible Remedy
Fluid is overheating	A. Excess flow over relief valve	1. Adjust pump gpm (variable volume pump) 2. Reduce pump rpm's. 3. Change to small gpm pump.
	B. System pressure too high	1. Lower system pressure.
	C. Contamination	1. Drain, clean and flush system.
	D. Improper valve size	1. Check for proper valve capacity. 2. Remove valve and replace with larger valve.
	E. Fluid is forced to travel both ways through needle valve	1. Add check valve to system. 2. Check valve stuck close.
	F. Needle valve installed backwards	1. Reverse connections.

When a check valve is installed in a circuit, it is generally considered the most effective sealing component in the circuit. The following charts point out some general problems that can occur with a check valve.

Problem	Probable Cause	Possible Remedy
No flow through valve	A. Broken spring	1. Disassemble & replace spring.
	B. Valve installed backwards	1. Reverse connection. 2. Check free-flow direction indicator.
	C. No pump flow	1. See Troubleshooting Pump section.
Actuator drifts	A. Seat or poppet damaged	1. Replace or refinish seat. 2. Replace poppet. 3. Check for excessive backpressure shock.
	B. Erosion of seat area.	1. Drain, clean & flush system. 2. Refill system with filtered fluid.
	C. Excessive leakage	1. Check leakage at cylinder at actuator or motor. 2. See Troubleshooting Cylinders and Motors sections.
No reverse flow through pilot operated valve	A. No or low pilot pressure	1. Check system pressure, increase as necessary. 2. Check for collapsed pilot line.
	B. Leakage at plunger piston seal	1. Disassemble and repair or replace.
	C. Plunger piston binding	1. Disassemble and clean valve. 2. Check for burrs on piston and/or bore.
Too high a pressure drop	A. Incorrect valve size	1. Change valve

CYLINDERS, MOTORS AND ACCUMULATOR MAINTENANCE

Hydraulic cylinders are by far the most common device used to convert fluid pressure into useful mechanical energy.

There are many types of cylinders available. The symbols show: single-acting, single-acting spring returned, double-acting differential, double-rod double-acting and telescoping.

What a Cylinder Consists Of

The basic hydraulic cylinder consists of cap or base end with port, cylinder body, piston with cast iron, steel or phenolic rings or lipseals; head or rod end with port and rod gland seals and bushing.

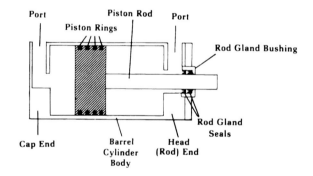

Cylinder operation such as speed and force are determined by the fluid volume and pressure respectively. Performance can be greatly affected by wear of the seals and bore. The problems that occur with cylinders are discussed below.

Piston Seal Leakage

As a cylinder operates in a system, cylinder seals wear resulting in leakage at the piston rod and across the cylinder piston. Leakage at the rod seal results in a housekeeping problem and can readily be detected. Seal leakage across the cylinder piston is not as easily determined.

In the next section, we find how piston leakage causes rod speed to decrease and may even cause intensification or reversal of motion in some cases. Then what checks can be made to determine if a piston seal is leaking excessively are examined.

Affects of Piston Leakage

As pointed out, piston seals are commonly cast iron rings or lipseals of a resilient synthetic rubber compound. Most heavy duty hydraulic cylinders are manufactured with cast iron piston rings. A small leakage across the piston is not normally a problem. Leakage of approximately 1 in^3/1000 psi/min. (16.38 cm^3/70.31 kg/cm^2/min).

Piston seal leakage is an obvious problem in a holding application. Also in an application of a horizontal cylinder with a large rod because, pressure can equalize on both sides of the piston and push the piston rod out.

Piston leakage can be a problem in clamping applications. When just one cylinder is involved it is not normally a problem.

However, when many cylinders are used on a machine in conjunction with a small pump, it may occur that the total leakage across all the cylinders is more than the pump's output and, therefore, it cannot generate sufficient holding pressure. This problem is quite noticeable with high water content fluids where the difference in viscosity becomes a factor. If cast iron rings are used and this problem occurs, switching to lipseals may cure it.

Intensification from Piston Leakage

In some cases, piston seal leakage can cause pressure intensification.

In the circuit illustrated, a cylinder in conjunction with a directional valve and pilot operated check valve is required to raise and hold a load in mid-stroke. The load is 6000 lbs. (2722 kg). The cylinder piston has an area of 6 in^2 and a 5 in^2 (32.26 cm^2) effective area.

The cylinder in the circuit has an excessive leakage problem at the piston seal. Excessive leakage at a piston rod is usually quite obvious and a housekeeping problem; assume the rod gland seals to be good. This leaves piston seal leakage.

When the directional valve is shifted, flow at a pressure of 1000 psi (70.31 kg/cm²) enters the cap end of the cylinder raising the load. As the float center directional valve is centered, the load gradually falls because of leakage across the piston, which is allowed to flow back to tank.

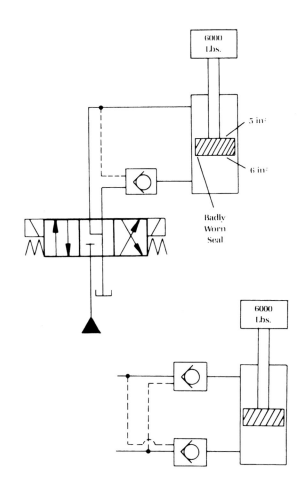

To remedy the problem, a pilot operated check valve is added to the rod-side cylinder line preventing flow from the rod-side back to tank. Now when the directional valve is centered, fluid is not allowed to escape from the cylinder. Since a seal basically does not exist across the piston, liquid volumes on either side of the piston can communicate. Without a piston seal, piston and piston rod can be considered immersed in the liquid.

It may be felt that since a piston has no seals, the load, piston rod, and piston will drift completely down even though fluid is trapped in the cylinder. This is not the case and may be explained by an example.

In the illustration, a piston and piston rod are immersed halfway in a cylinder filled with liquid. The piston has an area of 6 in² (38.71 cm²) and 5 in² (32.26 cm²) effective area. If the piston drifted down 1 in² (2.54 cm²), 6 in³ (98.32 cm³) of oil would be displaced (6 in² piston area x 1 in. stroke). At the other side of the piston, only a 5 in³ (81.9 cm³) space would be evacuated. Since 6 in³ (98.32 cm³) of oil does not fit into a 5 in³ (81.9 cm³) space, the piston cannot drift completely down unless some fluid leaks out of the cylinder.

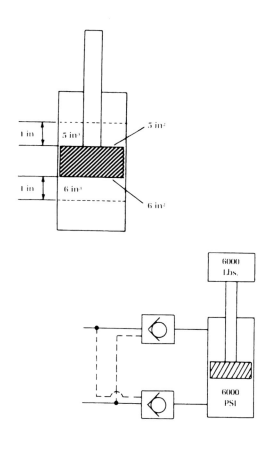

Returning to our problem, we find that with piston seals worn excessively, pressure on either side of the piston is equal. Pressure acting on the piston area is offset by pressure acting on the effective area except for an area equal to the rod cross-sectional area. This is the area which may support the load. Since rod area is 1 in² (6.45 cm²) and the load is 6000 lbs. (2722 kg), pressure generated in the cylinder is 6000 psi (421.84 kg/cm²).

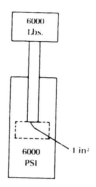

Another way of thinking of it would be to consider a rod immersed part way into a cylinder filled with liquid. If the rod had a cross-sectional area of 1 in² (6.45 cm²) and supported 6000 lbs. (2722 kg), 6000 psi (421.84 kg/cm²) would be generated in the cylinder. If a smaller-than-bore piston were attached to the rod, pressure would still be the same since any area of the piston not in contact with the rod would be cancelled out by equal pressure on both sides.

The generation of high pressure in this manner can be a source of ruptured rod gland seals, external leakage and other cylinder damage.

Checking for Piston Seal Leakage

Checking for piston seal leakage can be accomplished by seeing the effect of by-pass flow on rod speed.

To check for piston leakage, a needle or shut off valve is piped into the rod side cylinder line. With the valve closed and the piston bottomed against the cap end, the cap end of the cylinder is subjected to full system pressure. The valve is then cracked open allowing the piston to move a short distance along its stroke. The valve is then closed. At this point, full system pressure will act on the major area of the piston resulting in an intensified pressure at the rod side.

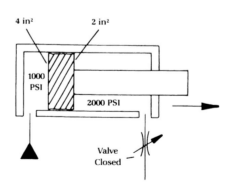

In the illustration, a 2:1 cylinder has a piston area of 4 in² (25.8 cm²) and an effective area of 2 in² (12.9 cm²). With the relief valve set at 1000 psi (70.31 kg/cm²) and the rod end cylinder port blocked, 4000 lbs. (1814 kg) (4 in² x 1000 psi) of force is generated on the piston major area to extend the rod. This 4000 lbs. (1814 kg) acts on the 2 in² (12.9 cm²) minor area of the piston resulting in 2000 psi (4000 lbs./2 in²) (140.61 kg/cm²) back-pressure at the rod side.

With 1000 psi (70.31 kg/cm²) at the cap end and 2000 psi (140.61 kg/cm²) at the rod end, any fluid leakage will transfer from the rod side to the cap end side causing the piston rod to drift out. This check is performed at regular intervals along the cylinder stroke.

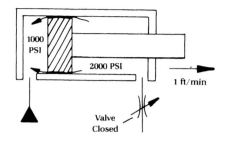

SAFETY NOTE: This method is not re-commended on systems where system pressure is 1500 psi or above. If using a large rod and no leakage occurs across the piston, it can result in pressures at the rod end of 3000 psi or higher, causing rod seal blow out or other damage to cylinder.

As a piston seal check is performed, the rate at which the rod drifts determines the reduction in rod speed as the cylinder operates in a system. In our illustrated 2:1 cylinder, assume that under test conditions, the rod drifted out at a rate of 1 ft/min with a 1000 psi (70.31 kg/cm²) differential across its piston. Therefore, with the cylinder operating in a system at a differential of 1000 psi (70.31 kg/cm²), a reduction in speed of 1 ft/min (.3048 m/min) can be expected. With the cylinder receiving 5 gpm (18.93 lpm), the piston rod would extend at a rate of 23.06 ft/min (7.19 m/min) because of this leakage. If the reduced rod speed caused by piston seal leakage cannot be tolerated, the cylinder should be repaired or replaced.

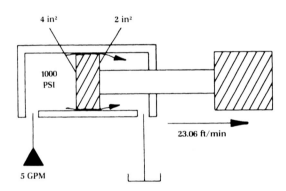

Keep in mind that the standard piston seals for hydraulic cylinders are cast iron piston rings. These seals leak 1-3 in³ (16.38-49.14 cm³) of oil per minute at a pressure of 1000 psi (70.31 kg/cm²). They are designed to leak somewhat for pur-pose of lubrication. This flow should not be confused with leakage flow due to wear.

In the next section, we find that an inten-sified pressure is present at the rod side of an unloaded, extending, single rod, double acting cylinder while flow is being metered out. This pressure can cause harm to a cylinder.

Intensification at Cylinder Rod Side

If a flow control valve is positioned at the rod side of a cylinder, this valve would restrict flow from the cylinder and as a result, the cylinder would not be allowed to run away from pump flow. This is known as a meter-out circuit.

The flow control valve kept the cylinder from running away by causing a back pressure to be generated on the minor area of the piston. The resultant force kept the piston and rod under control.

In any meter-out circuit in which a single rod, double acting cylinder is pushing out a load, pressure acting on the piston will be at full system pressure and its resultant force is more than required to equal the load. Whatever force is in excess develops a backpressure on the effective area.

In the illustration, a 2:1 cylinder is required to move a 6000 lb. (2722 kg) load. The major area of the piston is 4 in^2 (25.81 cm^2) and the minor area is 2 in^2 (12.9 cm^2). From the formula: pressure (psi) = force (lbs.)/area (in^2), or pressure (kg/cm^2) = force (kg)/area (cm^2), it can be calculated that 1500 psi (105.46 kg/cm^2) must act on the major area of the piston in order to equal the load. Assume now that pump flow is 10 gpm (37.85 lpm), relief valve setting is 2000 psi (140.61 kg/cm^2), and the flow control valve is set to meter 40 gpm (15.14 lpm) out of the cylinder as the rod extends.

With a 2:1 cylinder, if 10 gpm (37.85 lpm) enters the cap end, 5 gpm (18.93 lpm) discharges from the rod end when there is no flow control valve used. With the flow control set for 4 gpm (15.14 lpm), only 8 gpm (30.28 lpm) is allowed into the cylinder.

When pump/electric motor is turned on, pressure begins to build in the system.

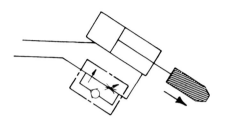

Meter-Out Circuit

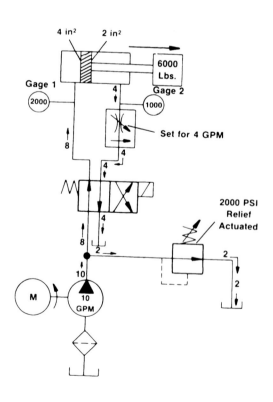

(This, of course, happens almost instantly.) When pressure reaches 1500 psi (105.46 kg/cm²), the load has been equalled. But, pump/electric motor cannot put its flow of 10 gpm (37.85 lpm) into the system at 1500 psi (105.46 kg/cm²). More pressure is developed -- 1600, 1700, 1800, 1900 psi (11.249, 119.52, 126.55, 133.58 kg/cm²). When pressure reaches 2000 psi (140.61 kg/cm²), the relief valve cracks open enough to pass 2 gpm (7.57 lpm). 10 gpm (37.85 lpm) discharges from the pump at 2000 psi (140.61 kg/cm²). 8 gpm (30.28 lpm) at 2000 psi (140.61 kg/cm²) heads toward the cylinder; 2 gpm (7.57 lpm) at 2000 psi (140.61 kg/cm²) dumps over the relief valve.

At this point in time, gage 1 at the cylinder cap end indicates 2000 psi (140.61 kg/cm²). 2000 psi (140.61 kg/cm²) on 4 in (25.81 cm²) results in 8000 lbs. (3629 kg) extending the piston rod. 6000 lbs. (2722 kg) is used to equal the load.

The 2000 lbs. (907.2 kg) in excess is offset by a 1000 psi (70.31 kg/cm²) backpressure on the 2 in² (12.9 cm²) minor area. The back pressure is generated as a result of the flow control valve restriction. Gage 2 indicates 1000 psi (70.31 kg/cm²).

If the same situation occurred with no load, the restriction of the flow control valve would cause an extremely high pressure to be generated.

In the circuit illustrated, our 2:1 cylinder extends rapidly to the work load. At a point near the work, a deceleration valve is closed off forcing fluid to pass through a flow control valve as it exits cylinder rod side. The rod continues to extend for a short distance and then contacts the work load.

Between the time the deceleration valve closes and the load is contacted, 8000 lbs. (3629 kg) of force is generated on the piston major area, but a load is not present to make use of it. This results in 8000 lbs. (3629 kg) being absorbed by a backpressure acting on 2 in² (12.9 cm²) (8000 lbs./2 in² = 4000 psi) or (3629

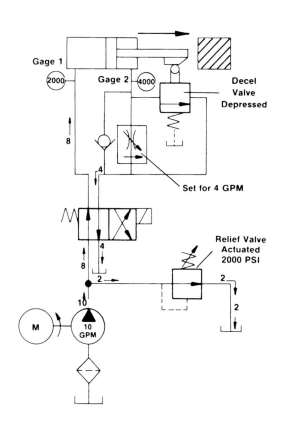

kg/129 cm² = 281.23 kg/cm²). Gage 2 indicates 4000 psi and continues to indicate 4000 psi (281.23 kg/cm²) until the load is contacted. Pressure intensification at the rod side of a cylinder can cause rod seals to leak or rupture.

Intensification can be expected to occur in the above manner anytime an extending, single rod, double acting cylinder is being metered out without a load. Since cylinder cushions are also metered-out restrictions, pressure intensification will occur anytime an extending, single rod, double acting cylinder goes into cushion. This does not affect the rod seal, but can cause leakage fluid to discharge from the needle valve cushion adjustment.

From previous illustrations, it has been shown that discharge flow from pump/electric motor is not necessarily the maximum flow rate in a system. The above example points out that a relief valve setting is not necessarily the maximum pressure in a system.

Cylinder Troubleshooting

There are basically two major areas of cylinder problems: erratic or slow cylinder operation and cylinder fails to move the load. The following charts cover these and other related problems.

Problem	Probable Cause	Possible Remedy
Cylinder drifts	A. Piston seal(s) leak	1. Disassemble & replace seals.
	B. Directional control valve leaks	1. Refer to section on directional control valve maintenance.
	C. Sufficiently high return line backpressure (Single acting cylinder)	1. Check for restricted return line. 2. Remove and replace return line filter.
	D. Common occurrence with closed center directional valve in neutral or center position and pump under load	1. Change to tandem spool type valve. 2. Unload the pump. 3. Change to valve with special notch design at land areas that prevent this pressure buildup.
Cylinder does not move the load when directional valve is actuated	A. Binding of linkage arrangement	1. Check linkage for proper alignment.
	B. Piston rod bent or broken	1. Disassemble and replace rod. 2. Check for proper mounting alignment.
	C. Piston seal(s) leak	1. Disassemble & replace seals.
	D. Pressure too low	1. Check & adjust system pressure.
	E. Cylinder too small	1. Recalculate cylinder size end load requirements.
	F. Contamination	1. Replace all worn and scored parts. 2. Flush, clean & refill system.
Leakage between body and end caps	A. Hard and/or brittle seals	1. Check for excessive operating temperature. 2. Remove and replace with heat tolerant seals.
	B. Pressure too high	1. Pressure should be lower, to adjusted rated limit. 2. Measure pressure inside cylinder during cushioning. Use external shock absorbing device.
	C. Crushed or extruded seal.	1. Remove and replace seal. 2. Lubricate seal before installation. 3. Retorque tie rods properly. Check manufacturer specifications.

Problem	Probable Cause	Possible Remedy
	D. Mushy or soft seals	1. Check seal and fluid compatibility. 2. Replace with seal that is compatible with fluid.
	E. Improperly torqued tie rods.	1. Retorque tie rods properly. Check manufacturer specifications.
	F. Wear or flat spots on seal inner and/or outer diameter	1. Check for side loading or for other causes of wear. 2. Replace seals.
Internal seal leakage	A. Extreme backpressure	1. Check flow control adjustment and correct if necessary. 2. Check internal cushion adjustment and correct if necessary.
	B. Soft or mushy seals	1. Check compatibility of seals and fluid. 2. Replace with compatible seals.
	C. Hard and brittle	1. Check for excessive operating temperature. 2. Remove and replace with heat tolerant seals.
	D. Improper installation	1. Disassemble and turn seals to to proper position.
	E. Excessive wear	1. Remove and replace seals. 2. Flush, clean & refill system. 3. Replace with more durable seals.
Rod gland seal leaks	A. Nicked, worn and/or scored rod and seals.	1. Check rod for damage; replace. 2. Check for normal seal wear with a .002 feeler between seals and rod. Should be tight.
	B. Loose retainer or bushing	1. Adjust retainer until leakage stops (V-packing) 2. Remove & replace V-packing.
	C. Hard and brittle	1. Check for excessive operating temperature. 2. Remove and replace with heat tolerant seals.
	D. Mushy or soft	1. Check compatibility of seals and fluid. 2. Replace with compatible seals.

Problem	Probable Cause	Possible Remedy
Cylinder operates erratically	A. Cylinder leaks internally.	1. Repair and/or replace parts and seals. 2. Check fluid viscosity using a visgage or through oil analysis. Compare to equipment manufacturer's specification. 3. Check for contamination. Flush, clean & refill system.
	B. Aeration of system	1. Bleed the system of air. 2. Check pump intake with vacuum gage. Fix any leaks. 3. Check for low fluid level. 4. Check for fluid return line in tank above fluid level. Extend return line.
	C. Directional valve not shifting completely	1. Disassemble and clean. Reassemble. 2. Check pilot pressure, too low. 3. Check for system aeration. 4. Check for contamination and wear.
	D. Low pilot pressure	1. Check choke control (if so equipped) for proper adjustment 2. Check source pressure. Adjust as needed. 3. Disassemble and clean valve passages.
	E. Cylinder binding or sticking	1. Disassemble and inspect for probable cause of sticking; clean and reassemble. 2. Readjust rod gland seal packing. 3. Realign linkage. 4. Check rod for bending. If necessary, check for proper rod size and if a stop tube is needed.

Hydraulic Motor Types

Hydraulic motors operate because of an imbalance within their rotating elements. Each motor type uses different elements by which this imbalance is generated.

Gear Motor

A simple, external gear motor basically consists of a housing with inlet and outlet ports, and a rotating group made up of two spur gears. One gear, the drive gear, is attached to a shaft which is connected to a load. The other gear is the driven or idler gear.

A gear motor has an imbalance resulting from pressure acting on meshed and un-meshed gear teeth. In the gear motor illustration, motor inlet is subjected to system pressure; motor outlet is under tank pressure. It can be seen that all unmeshed gear teeth subjected to system pressure are hydraulically balanced. At the point where gears mesh, one side of the gear tooth is sealed off from its following tooth (shaded area). This is the point of imbalance.

Another type of gear motor is an internal gear, commonly called a gerotor motor. The inner gear is the drive gear which is attached to a shaft and load. The outer or driven gear has one extra tooth. The imbalance created in the gerotor motor is caused by a difference in gear tooth area exposed to incoming hydraulic fluid pressure.

Vane Motor

A vane motor basically consists of a housing with inlet and outlet ports, and a rotating group made up of a rotor, vanes, cam ring, and port plate. Vanes are kept in contact with the cam ring by springs or fluid pressure. The rotor is attached to a shaft which is connected to a load.

A vane motor has an imbalance resulting from unequal vane areas being exposed to pressure. In the vane motor illustration, the

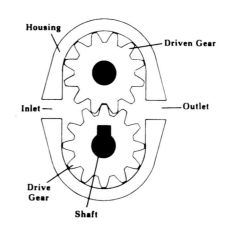

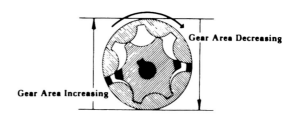

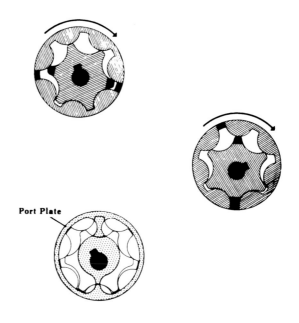

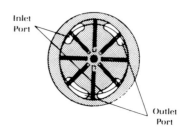

rotor is positioned in the center of a cam ring. A port plate separates incoming from outgoing fluid dividing the rotating group into four sections or quadrants. With vanes extended and pressure acting at motor inlet, it can be seen that vane area exposed to pressure increases at motor inlet as vanes move through the quadrant in a clockwise direction. More vane area is exposed to pressure at the end of the quadrant than at the beginning. This results in an imbalance within the inlet quadrants which develops torque at the motor shaft.

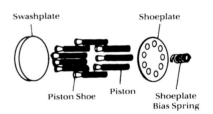

Axial Piston Motor

An axial piston motor consists of a housing with inlet and outlet ports, swashplate, cylinder barrel, pistons with shoes, shoeplate and bias spring, port plate and shaft.

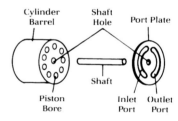

Pistons fit within bores of the cylinder barrel and are on the same axis as output shaft. Swashplate is positioned at an angle and acts as a surface on which piston shoes travel. Shoes are held in contact with the swashplate by shoeplate and bias springs. The port plate separates incoming from discharge fluid.

Rotation in an axial piston motor is generated as a result of swashplate angle. In the axial piston motor illustration, the swashplate is positioned at an angle which does not give a piston shoe a very stable surface on which to position itself. When system pressure acts on the single piston in the illustration, a force is developed which pushes the piston out of the cylinder barrel causing the piston shoe to slide across the swashplate surface. As the piston shoe slides, it causes the cylinder barrel and shaft to rotate and develops a torque at the motor shaft.

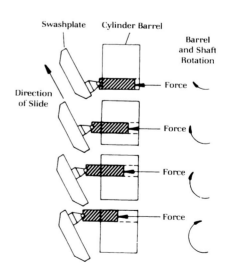

By varying the swashplate angle, axial piston motors can be made variable displacement and overcenter. With a variable displacement axial piston motor, output torque and shaft speed will vary as swashplate angle is changed. An overcenter axial piston motor has the capability of varying torque and speed as well as reversing shaft rotation without reversing the flow through the motor.

Piston motors are the only motor types which of themselves has an ability to vary output torque, shaft speed and rotation. Vane and gear motors do not have this ability. In the next section, we illustrate relationships between flow, pressure and motor displacement.

Motor Cavitation

The braking relief valve circuit shown with a closed center directional valve does not take into account that hydraulic motors can cavitate. A motor will cavitate just as a pump if an insufficient fluid supply is received at its inlet while turning. This means anytime a motor is braking, motor inlet must be opened to a fluid supply.

In a unidirectional motor circuit, motor inlet can be connected to a fluid supply through a position of a directional valve. In the circuit illustrated, a unidirectional motor is connected to a 2-position 4-way valve. The spring offset position has P and B blocked with A opened to tank. When braking occurs, motor outlet is blocked. Motor discharge flow is forced to pass over the braking relief valve. If a less-than-atmospheric pressure is generated at motor inlet, fluid is drawn up from the reservoir through the directional valve.

Make-up Check Valves

In a bi-directional motor circuit, supplying liquid to motor inlet during braking is usually done with low cracking pressure check valves [5 psi (352 kg/cm²)] or less. The checks are positioned in each motor line and are known as make-up check valves.

In the illustrated bi-directional motor circuit with one braking relief valve, make-up check valves are incorporated in the motor lines. Their orientation is opposite to the check valves serving the braking relief valves.

When braking is required with the load turning clockwise, flow passes over check

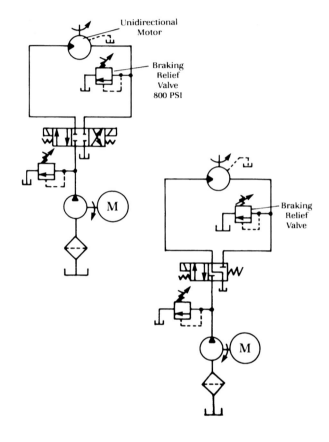

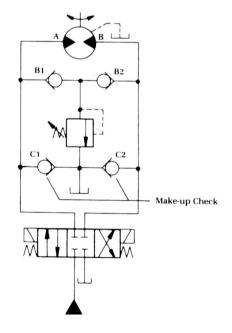

valve B2 through the relief valve back to tank. If a less-than-atmospheric pressure is generated at port A, make-up check valve C1 opens, drawing fluid from the reservoir. In opposite direction during braking, flow passes through check valve B1 through the relief valve back to tank. If a less-than-atmospheric pressure is generated at port B, make-up check valve C2 opens, drawing fluid from the reservoir.

Make-up check valves are very common components in motor circuits.

Crossover Relief Valves

A bi-directional motor circuit using braking relief valves in both directions can be designed so that discharge flow from the relief valves crosses over, or is connected to, the opposite motor line.

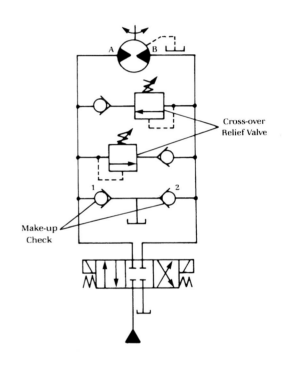

Cross-over Relief Valve

Make-up Check

From first glance, it may appear that these "crossover" relief valves would keep motor inlet well supplied since motor discharge flow is redirected to motor inlet. This might be the case with an internally drained motor whose shaft seal operated properly and whose directional valve did not leak. With an externally drained motor, however, make-up checks are still required. Because drainage flow separates from discharge flow, fluid required to fill motor inlet will not be equal to fluid flow discharging motor outlet. The arrangement of crossover relief valves and make-up check is a very common bi-directional motor circuit.

Hydraulic Motor Wear

Hydraulic motors wear just as pumps or any other rotating elements. Wear in a hydraulic motor shows up as increased leakage and reduced shaft speed.

As illustrated earlier, while motors operate, internal leakage is generated by pressure differential across clearances of stationary parts or rotating elements. In a gear motor, this occurs between gear teeth, side plates and housing. In a vane motor, leakage appears between rotor, vanes, cam ring and port plate. In a piston motor, leakage oc-

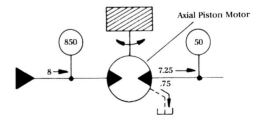

Axial Piston Motor

curs between cylinder barrel, pistons and port plate.

As wear increases, leakage increases especially across rotating elements. With the same flow entering a worn motor, shaft speed decreases. Approximately the same pressure is required to equal load resistances; but, since leakage paths have increased in size, motor flow can be pushed through the clearance with the same pressure.

Finally, if wear is allowed to continue, a point is reached where all inlet flow goes into leakage at a pressure less than work pressure. This results in no movement at the motor shaft.

Assume a load requires 800 psi (56.25 kg/cm^2) differential across a motor to equal resistances. As wear causes leakage to increase, motor speed decreases. Finally, when the motor is excessively worn, a pressure differential of less than 800 psi (56.25 kg/cm^2) can push all incoming flow back to tank. The motor stalls.

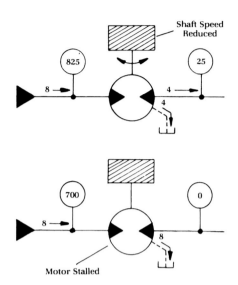

Shaft Speed Reduced

Motor Stalled

Check for Hydraulic Motor Wear

A check for hydraulic motor wear is performed by comparing drain flows and/or shaft speeds. With an externally drained axial piston motor, all internal leakage discharges through the drain. If drain flow is excessive as compared to original conditions, motor wear is excessive. This can be checked with a flow meter.

Since the external drain of gear or vane motors only indicates leakage through clearance of stationary parts, drain flow could have increased relatively little between original and worn conditions.

However, fluid bypassing gears and vanes could have increased significantly. Motor wear in these motors can be only indirectly determined by comparing present motor shaft speeds with original shaft speed. The same is true with an internally drained motor, since leakage is not separated from motor discharge at all. When making these checks, be sure that the motor flows and

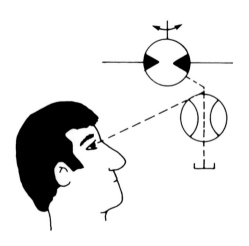

speeds are compared against the original
or new motor flows and speed. That is,
operate the motor at the same pressure
and the same load as when it was new.

Problem	Probable Cause	Possible Remedy
Excessive motor noise	A. Motor-load coupling misaligned	1. Realign motor and load coupling to within .005 in. T.I.R.
	B. Motor running away	1. Add flow control to outlet. 2. Reduce load.
	C. Aeration	1. Check for foaming oil. 2. Flush, clean & refill system with fluid having anti-foam additives.
	D. Cavitation	1. Reduce motor speed. 2. Check viscosity of fluid. Too high, change to fluid recommended by motor manufacturer. 3. Preheat fluid. 4. Check for restricted inlet. 5. Check for open brake, crossover or make-up valve. 6. Check hydraulic pump for cavitation.
	E. Case drain restricted	1. Check drain line, remove and replace.
	F. Sticking vane (on vane motors)	1. Disassemble, clean and reassemble. 2. Check for proper vane positioning.
	G. Worn or broken parts	1. Disassemble, replace parts and reassemble. 2. Replace motor.
Motors runs excessively hot	A. Inlet oil is hotter than normal	1. Check for problem at pump. (See Pump Troubleshooting section. 2. Wrong viscosity oil. 3. Check oil coolers for obstruction or insufficient cooling capacity. 4. Check for low oil level.
	B. Motor slippage too high	1. Disassemble and inspect motor elements; replace if worn or damaged.
	C. Drain line restricted	1. Remove and replace.
	D. High GPM flow rate over relief valve	1. Reduce pump output. 2. Readjust flow control valve.
Motor rotates in wrong direction	A. Piping incorrect from directional control valve	1. Check piping drawing and correct.
	B. Wiring or directional control valve incorrect	1. Check wiring diagram and correct.
	C. Incorrect valve spool (Tandem instead of motor)	1. Disassemble, remove and exchange spools. 2. Change valve.

Problem	Probable Cause	Possible Remedy
Motor will not rotate	A. Load binding	1. Check for linkage and/or other misalignment. 2. Loosen and retorque motor mounting bolts.
	B. Open brake, crossover, make-up or system relief valve(s)	1. Check for any or all pressure control valves bypassing fluid to tank. Remove, repair and/or replace valve(s).
	C. Low operating pressure	1. Check system pressure, make necessary adjustments.
	D. Motor displacement adjustment not set properly (Variable speed & torque motors)	1. Set adjustment to proper motor displacement angle. 2. Set at maximum displacement and then decrease to desired speed and/or torque.
	E. Pump not delivering proper volume and/or pressure.	1. Refer to Pump Troubleshooting section.
	F. Seized motor parts.	1. Disassemble, repair or replace parts. 2. Replace motor.
Load drifts	A. External brake needed	1. Consider the addition of a brake; all hydraulic motors have internal leakage allowing load drift.
	B. External brake failure	1. Check out the cause of the brake or failure.

Accumulator Types

Hydraulic accumulators can be divided into weight-loaded, spring-loaded or hydro-pneumatic. Each classification identifies by what means an accumulator maintains a force on a liquid while it is stored.

Weight-loaded Accumulator

A weight-loaded accumulator maintains a force on the liquid it stores by means of heavy weights acting on a piston or ram. The weights can be made of any heavy material such as iron, concrete or even a liquid. Weight-loaded accumulators are generally quite large, in some cases holding hundreds of gallons. They can service several hydraulic systems at one time and are most often used in mill and central hydraulic systems.

A desirable characteristic of a weight-loaded accumulator is that it stores fluid under a relatively constant pressure whether it is full or nearly empty; this will not be the case in other accumulator types. Because the weight applying the force to the liquid does not change, the same force is applied regardless of how much liquid is present in the accumulator.

An undesirable characteristic of a weight-loaded accumulator is shock generation. When a weight-loaded accumulator, discharging quickly, is suddenly stopped, the inertia of the weight could cause excessive pressure surges in a system. This can result in leaking fluid conductors and fittings, and early component failure due to metal fatigue.

Spring-loaded Accumulator

A spring-loaded accumulator applies a force to its stored liquid by means of a spring acting on a piston.

Spring-loaded medium and high pressure accumulators are typically smaller than weight-loaded accumulators with

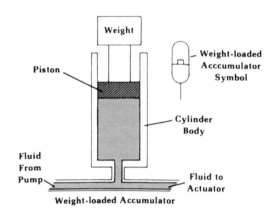

Weight-loaded Accumulator

sizes holding up to several gallons. Spring-loaded accumulators usually serve individual hydraulic systems and generally operate at low pressure.

As liquid is pumped into a spring-loaded accumulator, the stored fluid pressure is determined by the compression rate of the spring. An accumulator of this type will have more stored pressure with the piston moved up and the spring compressed 10 inches than if it were only compressed 4 inches. To avoid accumulation of leakage fluid, the spring chamber of a spring-loaded accumulator is vented. Leakage fluid will eventually discharge from the vent hold. This will give a good indication of the internal condition of the accumulator.

Spring-loaded accumulators are not externally drained back to tank because they can cause oil foaming. With an external drain terminating either above or below fluid level, leakage accumulated above the piston will tend to foam during accumulator operation. As the accumulator discharges rapidly, fluid above the piston will be unable to keep up with piston movement. A less-than-atmospheric pressure will be generated in the spring chamber resulting in dissolved air coming out of the liquid. When the accumulator is recharged, the piston moves up, pushing the aerated oil to tank.

For this reason, spring-loaded accumulators are not generally externally drained. With spring chamber vented, spring-loaded accumulators demand immediate attention once their piston seals wear. If maintenance is not performed on a spring-loaded accumulator with a poor seal, a housekeeping problem could arise.

Hydro-pneumatic Accumulator

A hydro-pneumatic accumulator is the most commonly used accumulator in industrial hydraulic systems. This type accumulator applies a force to a liquid by using an inert compressed gas.

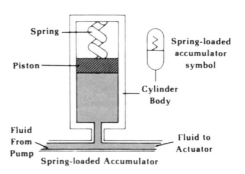

Spring-loaded Accumulator

Hydro-Pneumatic Accumulator Symbol

NOTE: In most cases of hydro-pneumatic accumulators applied to industrial systems, an inert gas, like dry nitrogen is used. Compressed air and especially oxygen should never be used because of the danger of exploding an air-oil vapor.

Hydro-pneumatic accumulators are divided into piston, diaphragm and bladder types. The name of each type indicates the device separating gas from liquid.

Piston Type Accumulator

A piston type accumulator consists of a cylinder body and moveable piston with resilient seals. Gas occupies the volume above the piston and is compressed as the cylinder body is charged with fluid. As fluid discharges from the accumulator, gas pressure pushes the piston down. When all liquid has been discharged, the piston should have reached the end of its stroke.

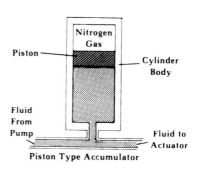

Piston Type Accumulator

Diaphragm Type Accumulator

A diaphragm type accumulator consists of two metal hemispheres which are bolted together, but whose interior volume is separated by a synthetic rubber diaphragm. On one side of the diaphragm, gas occupies the space. As fluid enters the other chamber, gas is compressed. Gas pressure drops as fluid discharges. Once all liquid has been discharged, the diaphragm covers the outlet retaining the gas within the accumulator.

The diaphragm will not be pushed through the outlet because of the outlet design and the thickness of the diaphragm.

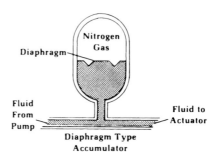

Diaphragm Type Accumulator

Bladder Type Accumulator

A bladder type accumulator consists of a synthetic rubber bladder inside a metal shell; the bladder contains the gas. As fluid enters the shell, gas in the bladder is compressed. Gas pressure decreases

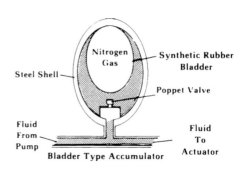

Bladder Type Accumulator

as fluid flows from the shell. When all liquid has been discharged, gas pressure attempts to push the bladder through the outlet. But, as the bladder contacts the poppet valve at the outlet, flow from the shell is automatically shut off.

Precharge

The gas pressure present in a hydropneumatic accumulator when it is drained of hydraulic fluid is the accumulator precharge. This pressure significantly affects a hydro-pneumatic accumulator's useable volume and operation as a shock absorber.

Precharge Affects Shock Absorber Operation

Precharge of a hydro-pneumatic accumulator affects its operation as a shock absorber. Shock generation in a hydraulic system is the result of fast pressure rises due to an external mechanical force acting on a cylinder or hydraulic motor, or the result of liquid crashing into a component as a valve is suddenly closed. An accumulator acts to reduce a shock effect by limiting pressure rise.

In a hydraulic system, as shock pressures develop, these high pressures attempt to displace or push the fluid to another part of the system. But, since liquid is relatively incompressible, it won't move or compress. Without an accumulator in the line, shock pressures can climb to a high value.

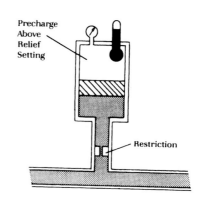

Above a certain system pressure as shock pressure begins to build, an accumulator absorbs the volume of liquid the shock attempts to compress or displace. The line in which the accumulator is located becomes compressible above a certain point.

Gas precharge for a hydro-pneumatic accumulator used as a shock absorber is generally set slightly above the maximum working pressure of the line in which it is located. If the maximum pressure happens to be determined by the relief valve setting, gas precharge might be 100 psi above this.

As an accumulator operates in a system as a shock absorber, it is generally required to get rid of the fluid it has accumulated in a controlled fashion. Commonly, accumulators in these applications are once again equipped with a restriction and bypass check valve. With this arrangement, an accumulator can accept its required fluid, yet any fluid accumulation can bleed off through the restriction.

Since proper gas precharge is such an important factor in hydro-pneumatic accumulator operation, we find in the following section how an accumulator can lose its precharge and how precharge pressure can be checked.

Losing Gas Precharge

Just because a hydro-pneumatic accumulator is charged once to the proper gas precharge, it does not mean it will remain charged to that pressure indefinitely. As accumulators operate, gas pressure can seep out through the gas valve. This can be due to a faulty or deteriorated seal in the valve, or an improperly seating poppet in the valve core.

Hydro-pneumatic accumulators also lose gas precharge when discharging fluid. With bladder and diaphragm type accumulators, this usually occurs in a catastrophic manner as a result of a rupture in the synthetic rubber separator. When a piston type accumulator discharges, gas pressure can escape across the piston due to worn seal. Piston type accumulators give an indication of wear as gas precharge gradually dissipates.

Checking Gas Precharge

Since proper gas precharge is an important consideration in hydro-pneumatic accumulator performance, precharge should be checked periodically.

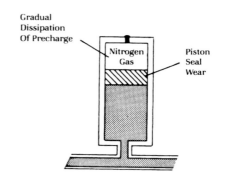

Gradual Dissipation Of Precharge

Nitrogen Gas

Piston Seal Wear

A necessary piece of equipment for checking gas pressure is a precharging and gaging assembly. This assembly is primarily made up of a gas chuck bleeder valve and pressure gage.

To check precharge, discharge the accumulator of liquid and remove the protective cap which frequently is found on the valve in the accumulator top.

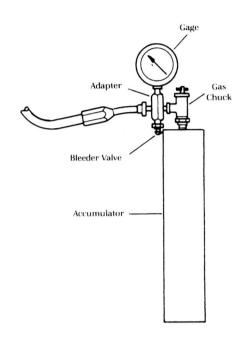

Screw the gas chuck handle of the assembly all the way out; check to see that the bleeder valve is closed. Attach the assembly to the accumulator gas valve at the gas chuck. Using a wrench, tighten gas chuck swivel nut securely onto gas valve. Turn gas chuck stem in; this depresses the core in the accumulator gas valve registering a gage pressure. This is the accumulator precharge.

If the accumulator is properly charged, back the gas chuck handle out and open the bleeder valve venting the assembly. Loosen the gas chuck swivel nut and remove the assembly. Replace the accumulator gas valve protective cover. If it is found that the accumulator is overcharged, excess pressure can be bled off through the bleeder valve.

If it is necessary to increase the gas pressure, back the gas chuck handle out. Open the bleeder valve venting the assembly; then reclose the bleeder valve. At this point, the charging assembly will have to be connected to a nitrogen bottle.

With the nitrogen bottle gas valve off, connect a hose from the bottle gas valve to the charging assembly gas valve. Turn the gas chuck completely in depressing the accumulator core. Crack open the gas valve of the nitrogen bottle to slowly fill the accumulator. Shut off the valve when the gage indicates the desired pressure.

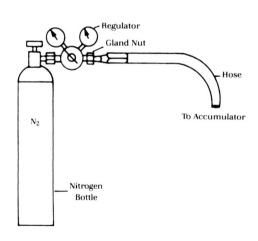

Once the gage indicates the appropriate pressure, shut off the bottle gas valve, turn out the gas chuck handle, open the gas bleeder valve. The charging hose and gaging assembly can then be removed.

Accumulator Troubleshooting

There are four major problems that affect the operation of an accumulator.

Caution when Disassembling Accumulator

Before working on a hydro-pneumatic accumulator, there are several precautionary measures that must be followed:

1. Before removing an accumulator from the system, be sure to release both hydraulic and gas pressures.

2. Before disassembling an accumulator, be sure the gas and fluid pressure have been released.

3. When disassembled, be careful not to allow dirt or other abrasive material to enter any opening.

4. When charging an accumulator, NEVER exceed the manufacturer's recommended specification.

5. NEVER FILL OR PRESSURIZE your accumulator with compressed air or oxygen. Should these gases mix with the fluid under pressure, an explosion could occur.

6. When reinstalling accumulator into the hydraulic system, some type of automatic bleed-off circuit for the accumulator should also be installed. A bleed-off circuit should always be designed into the hydraulic system in such a manner that when the equipment is shut down, a valve dumps the hydraulic fluid which was stored under pressure in the accumulator.

Problem	Probable Cause	Possible Remedy
Response of accumulator is slow	A. Precharge is too low	1. Check precharge pressure and recharge as necessary.
	B. Piston binding	1. Discharge gas pressure and fluid pressure. Be certain that both are at ambient atmospheric.
	C. Weak spring(s)	1. Disassemble and replace spring(s).
	D. Hydraulic line size too small	1. Resize, remove and replace.
Long pump-up time	A. Precharge too low or no precharge pressure	1. Check precharge pressure and recharge as necessary.
	B. Low pump volume	1. Check GPM output of pump. (See Pump Troubleshooting section.)
	C. Weak spring(s)	1. Disassemble and replace spring(s).
	D. Unloading valve set too low	1. Adjust valve to higher setting.
	E. Relief valve set too low or partially stuckopen	1. Adjust valve to higher setting. setting. 2. Remove, repair or replace valve.
Accumulator fails to absorb shock pressures	A. Precharge is lost	1. Check precharge pressure, recharge if necessary.
	B. Precharge is too high	1. Same as above.
	C. Diaphragm or bladder ruptured	1. Check for operating fluid temperature too high. Reduce temperature. 2. Bladder pinched when installed. Replace following manufacturer's installation procedure carefully.
	D. Piston seized	1. Disassemble and repair or replace.
	E. Hydraulic line size is too small	1. Resize, remove and replace.
Will not hold precharge	A. Ruptured diaphragm or bladder.	1. Disassemble and replace.
	B. Charging valve leaks	1. Remove and replace.
	C. Piston seal, diaphragm or bladder leaks	1. Check compatibility of fluid and rubber material. 2. Disassemble and replace. 3. Clean, flush & refill system.
	D. Loose body assembly bolts (diaphragm type)	1. Torque bolts to proper tightness.

LEAKAGE ELIMINATION IN HYDRAULIC SYSTEMS

Leakage has to be Eliminated Because

Leakage has to be eliminated in the hydraulic system because it increases the cost of operating the system by the loss of fluids and slippery floors are dangerous. Throughout the year, plants all over the world waste millions of gallons of fluid. In addition to fluid cost, the cost of reworking the system and constant maintenance increase your overall operating cost.

Beyond operating cost, you must consider lost business by opening doors to foreign products that may be more leak free; by opening doors to competing technologies; by missing delivery dates due to downtime caused by leakage, etc.

Reasons for Leakage

Leakage in a hydraulic system occurs because of four main reasons:

1. Poor system design
2. Substandard component quality
3. Improper installation
4. Abuse

Each one of these areas will be looked at in detail.

System Design: Component Selection-Fitting Style

Eight basic fitting connection types (four tube/hose connections and four port connections) can be chosen from for installation in your hydraulic system.

There is the 37° flare fitting (SAE J514), the inch flareless fitting (SAE J514), the more recent o-ring face seal (O.R.F.S.) (SAE 1453), and metric flareless fitting (ISO 8434-1). The four port connections are the pipe thread

(NPTF), SAE straight-thread (SAE J1926), SAE/ISO four bolt-flange (SAE J518) and metric straight thread (ISO 6149).

37° Flare (For Inch or Metric Tubing)

The 37° flare fitting is the most widely used type of fitting. This fitting has been used in industry for quite some time, so many people are familiar with it. This fitting is designed to be used in systems with average operating pressure of 3,000 PSI. Also, it is used with tubing which has a low to medium wall thickness. Thick wall tubing is very difficult to flare so it is not recommended with a flare fitting. The 37° flare fitting is suitable to be used in systems which operate between -65°F to 500°F with carbon steel tubing. The flare fitting occupies less space than most other fittings and it can easily be adapted to metric tubing. This fitting is readily available and is one of the lowest in installed cost. The nut draws the sleeve towards the flare and causes a positive seal between the flared tube face and the fitting body.

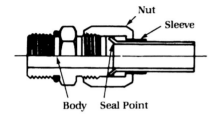

Flareless (For Inch Tubing)

The flareless fitting is very popular in certain markets in the United States. The flareless fitting is suitable to be used with both hydraulics and pneumatics and has an average working pressure to 3000 PSI. The flareless fitting must be used on either medium or heavy walled tubing because when the ferrule is properly seated, it penetrates into the tube wall. The flareless fitting requires minimal tube preparation. The nut forces the sleeve against the tapered seat, causing the front edge of sleeve to bite into the tube and creating a positive seal.

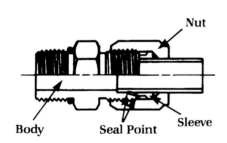

Multiple Bite Flareless (For Metric Tubing)

The multiple bite fitting has a ferrule with two cutting edges. One bite, the leading edge bite, is visible in the front; you can't see the second

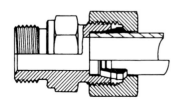

bite. This double bite gives the fitting a higher pressure capacity. The operating principle is similar to the fitting with a single bite ferrule.

Face Seal with O-ring
(For Inch or Metric Tubing)

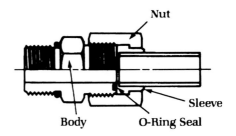

The face seal fitting is best suited for hydraulics and pneumatics and it can be used on any wall thickness tubing. Also, it can be used in systems which operate at 6000 PSI or less and in systems which are subjected to high frequency vibrations. After the sleeve is attached to the tube by brazing or flanging*, the nut is tightened to the body. The o-ring provides a positive seal between the sleeve and the body. The fitting can be repeatedly assembled and disassembled without affecting the seal. This fitting can easily be adapted to metric fastening tubing by using an adapter sleeve.

*Flanging is a faster, cleaner and less expensive way, developed by Parker, for attaching sleeve to the tube.

Pipe Thread Port Connections

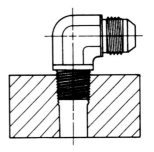

Pipe threads are a tapered thread which rely on the force generated by the taper to provide a seal between the threads. They require a thread sealer to assure a positive seal. Also, this fitting is prone to loosening and/or cracking when there is vibration and temperature cycling in the system (thermal expansion and contraction varies with different metals which will cause the threads to loosen). Because the threads are tapered, repeated assembly and disassembly can cause the threads to distort, leading to leakage. If the fitting is used in a cast iron port, overtightening can cause the port boss to crack.

Straight Thread with O-ring
(Inch and Metric Threads)

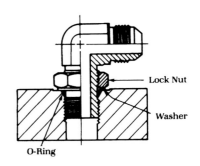

Straight threads are preferred over pipe threads because they rely on an o-ring to provide a positive seal. The o-ring seats on a spot face or in a cavity around the port; a jam nut locks the fitting into position. This assembly is much

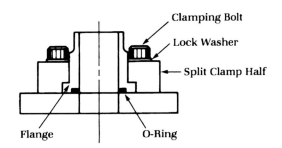

Clamping Bolt
Lock Washer
Split Clamp Half
Flange
O-Ring

less susceptible to vibrational and thermal loosening than pipe threads. Elbows and tees can be positioned easily because the jam nut on an adjustable fitting can be tightened with the fitting in any position. The fitting can be assembled and disassembled repeatedly without causing damage to the seal. The chance of contamination is minimal with the o-ring seal because there is no need for thread sealing compounds to create the seal, as is the case with pipe threads.

4-bolt Split Flange

The 4-bolt split flange fitting is a face seal type connection especially suited for large port sizes and high pressure systems. It is good for use in hard to reach areas and it has all the same advantages as a straight thread o-ring connection.

Even with these advantages, the 4-bolt split flange does take up a lot more space on the component it is mounted onto, and installation is more time consuming and careless torquing of the mounting bolts can cause other problems than just leaks.

Component Selection - Tube Type

Once the type of fittings to be used in your hydraulic system have been selected, you must select the type of tubing to go with the fittings. Not all tubing is suitable for use with all fittings.

There are three major types of tubing available for steel:

1. Welded flash controlled (SAE J356) - It is **not** suitable for flared fittings and only marginally suitable for flareless. It is best suited for brazed on face or flanged seal fittings.

2. Welded and Drawn (SAE J525) - is suitable for all styles of fittings.

3. Seamless (SAE J524) - works well with flareless and face seal fittings, but is **not** as good as welded and drawn (J525) for flared fittings because of occasional concentricity problems.

Component Interchangeability

One of the main criteria for component interchangeability is their design (dimensional) standard. These standards need to be coupled with performance standards to assure trouble-free hydraulic systems.

Such standards as published by SAE, NFPA, ASTM and ISO are all aimed at providing safe and effective component interchangeability.

System Design-Routing

When routing piping runs, maintaining joint accessibility is important for proper tightening and servicing of the joints and leakage prevention.

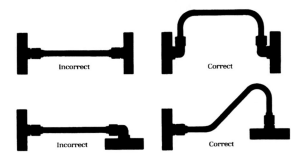

Avoid Excessive Strain

Although the shortest distance between any two points is a straight line, you may find that because of machine movement, pressure surges, vibrations and temperature changes, a straight piece of tubing can place an excessive amount of strain on the fittings. By bending the tube on short runs as illustrated, the strain is lessened or even eliminated, thus preventing leaks at the fittings.

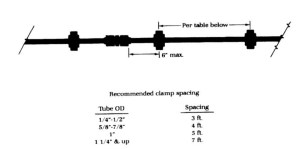

Recommended clamp spacing

Tube OD	Spacing
1/4"-1/2"	3 ft.
5/8"-7/8"	4 ft.
1"	5 ft.
1 1/4" & up	7 ft.

Use Proper Clamping

Using proper clamping to dampen vibration reduces potential leakage at joints. It is recommended that clamps with resilient inserts be used as illustrated.

When long runs are required, clamp supports should be positioned at various distances

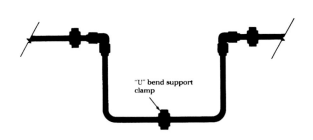

"U" bend support clamp

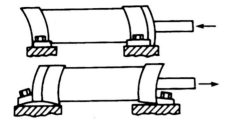

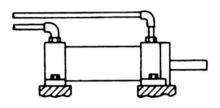

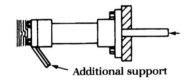

Additional support

along the run according to the tubing outer diameter size.

Also, in long runs of tubing you must take into consideration expansion and contraction of the tubing due to pressure surges and temperature variations. To compensate for this, it is recommended that a "U" bend or hose be placed in the line.

Allow for Movement Under Load

Another consideration when routing hydraulic systems is to anticipate a certain amount of movement by a system which is under load. For example, a design must acknowledge that cylinders under pressure and temperature changes elongate and contract. In addition, flexing and rocking makes the mounting method important. A foot-mounted cylinder, for example, may triple or quadruple leakage problems because of swinging motion of the heads.

Cylinders with non-centerline-type mountings tend to change length and sway under load and temperature change. Any rigid tubing connected to the cylinder heads will be subject to the resulting forces and motion. Leakage at the port threads is inevitable —regardless of whether they are tapered pipe or straight thread ports. An "S" bend in the tubing, as illustrated, is recommended to minimize the strain on fittings.

Cylinders with non-centerline mountings often require stronger machine members to resist bending, so consider the rigidity of the machine frame. For example, where on end of a cylinder must be overhung, an additional supporting member should be provided.

Component Quality - Fitting Quality

Check for nicks and burrs on the surfaces and threads. These will cause thread binding and poor sealing.

If you've selected fittings that use o-rings, be certain to check the condition of the o-ring as well as the contact areas of the fitting. Cracks or nicks in the o-ring will decrease the entire fitting's ability to prevent leaks.

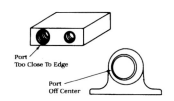

Tubing Quality

Proper size and roundness along with ductility are critical areas for all types of fittings. Surface quality of the outside dimension is very important for the flareless fittings while interior surface quality and concentricity are important for 37° flare fittings. Face seal fittings are more tolerant of inside and outside surface imperfections.

Mating Ports Quality

Inspection of the ports should be done to insure that they are located in such a manner as to provide sufficient strength and surface area for the fitting to seal properly.

Prying poorly bent tube in place strains the joint making it more prone to leakage

Installation - Tube Bends

The assembly of tubing and fittings is critical to leakage elimination within a hydraulic system. This portion of the presentation deals with tube preparation for the types of fittings discussed earlier and proper assembly techniques for fittings attached to tubing and ports.

Proper tube bending is essential in optimizing hydraulic system efficiency. Poorly bent tubes which are pried into place cause unnecessary stress on the fittings making them prone to leakage.

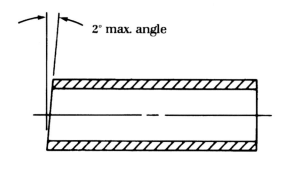

2° max. angle

Tubing Cutting

One of the first steps in preparing tubing for assembly to the fitting is to cut the tubing end square. To do this, two methods can be used. The recommended method is to use a power cutoff saw using a toothed cutoff wheel. The other method is use of a hacksaw and saw guide. A properly cut tube is necessary for all fittings.

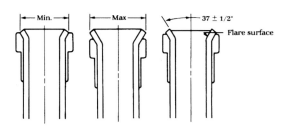

As illustrated, the maximum allowable angle for a cut tube end is 2°.

Tube Flaring

When using 37° flared fittings, the tube end must be flared properly. Flaring can be accomplished by using a suitable flaring tool. The flare should be 37° ±½°.

Check your flared tube for proper size by sliding the outside sleeve into place. The outside flare diameter should not exceed the outside sleeve diameter, likewise it should not be less than the inside taper of the sleeve.

The inside surface of your tube flare should also be checked for imperfections such as burrs, nicks, cracks and splits. These will reduce the fittings ability to seal properly.

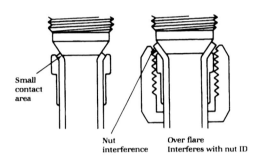

Small contact area

Nut interference

Over flare Interferes with nut ID

Under and Overflaring

Improper flaring can result in a condition of underflaring or overflaring. Underflaring will result in insufficient surface area for contact between tube and fitting, while overflaring can interfere with the fitting nut.

Underflaring can result in nose collapse and leakage, and overflaring poses fitting assembly problems.

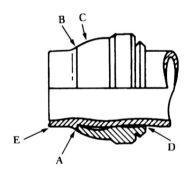

Flareless Preset

The use of flareless fittings does not require flaring of the tube end. To be effective, care must be taken when presetting (attaching) the ferrule to the tube. A proper preset should have the following characteristics:

A. Ridge on the tube raised to at least 50% of ferrule's front edge thickness.
B. The leading edge of the ferrule coined flat.
C. A slight bow formed at remaining part of barrel.
D. The back end of ferrule should be snug against tube.

E. There should be a slight indentation 360° around the end of the tube caused by the tube being bottomed out during assembly.

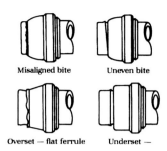

Misaligned bite   Uneven bite

Overset — flat ferrule   Underset —

Improper Flareless Preset

Illustrated are four improperly preset or misaligned ferrules. All of them can result in a leaky joint.

- An **uneven bite** occurs when the ferrule fails to seal along its original cut in the tube.
- A **misaligned bite** occurs when the ferrule is cocked when secured.
- **Overset** or a flat ferrule is caused by over-pressuring or overtightening the nut during preset.
- **Underset** is caused by low pressure or undertightening the nut during preset.

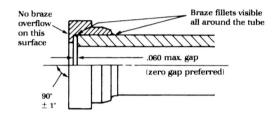

No braze overflow on this surface

Braze fillets visible all around the tube

.060 max. gap
(zero gap preferred)

90°
± 1°

Face Seal Brazing

The face seal with o-ring provides the highest degree of leak resistance when assembled properly.

It is necessary for the sleeve of the face seal to be properly brazed to the tube or leakage may occur. When a sleeve is properly brazed to a tube, these characteristics should exist:

- The sleeve should be positioned onto the tube with no more than .060" gap. Preferably zero gap should exist.
- Sleeve face must be perpendicular to center line of tube (90° ± 1°).
- There should be no braze overflow on the face of the sleeve.
- The braze fillets should be visible all around the tube.

Improper Brazing

An improper braze leads to a leaking joint. Should leakage occur, disassemble joint and check for:

- Improper placement or misalignment of the sleeve over the tube.

Size	Steel Torque (lb.-in.)	Stainless Steel Torque (lb.-in.)
*2	40 ± 5	50 ± 5
*3	70 ± 10	80 ± 10
4	140 ± 10	160 ± 10
*5	180 ± 15	225 ± 15
6	250 ± 15	325 ± 25
8	470 ± 25	625 ± 25
10	650 ± 50	800 ± 25
12	1050 ± 50	1300 ± 50
*14	1250 ± 50	1500 ± 50
16	1450 ± 50	1700 ± 50
20	2250 ± 100	2550 ± 100
24	3000 ± 150	3400 ± 200
32	3800 ± 200	4400 ± 200

*Estimated   NOTE: Dry Conditions

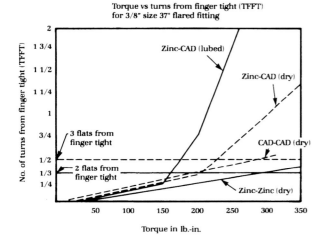

Torque vs turns from finger tight (TFFT)
for 3/8" size 37° flared fitting

- Poor braze joint caused by improper cleaning and/or fluxing, uneven or insufficient heat.
- Braze overflow on the sealing surface.

Assembly of Tube to 37° Flare Fitting - Torque Method

This portion of the lesson deals with the various methods of assembly for each of the fittings described earlier.

The torque method is used to properly tighten 37° flared fittings. Once the tube and fitting are aligned, tighten the nut to the torque recommended by the manufacturer. The chart shows representative torque values for 37° flared fitting for dry torquing. Under-torquing will result in poor contact between the flare and fitting nose, overtorquing can damage the flare or sleeve; either condition may result in a leaky joint.

The size of the fitting is given as a dash size which indicates the tube size in 16th. For example, size 4 indicates 4/16" or 1/4" inch tube OD.

Assembly of Mixed Platings on 37° Flare Fitting

The plating combination between the nut and the body changes the friction between the two surfaces. For a given torque, the amount of turns will vary.

As illustrated in this graph, a 3/8" flared fitting requires 275 lb.-in. of dry torque for proper seating and for the prevention of leakage when both the nut and body are cadmium plated; this torque produces a rotation of 3 flats from finger tight. While the same size fitting using different platings such as zinc and cadmium (dry) must be turned more than twice as many flats to achieve the same 275 lb.-in. of torque.

Although both plating combinations are torqued to equal value, the amount of crush created by the zinc-cad combination could damage the fitting leading to leakage. It is, therefore, recommended that plating material be the same between body and nut; check with the manu-facturer for type of plating used.

The alternate method of assembly described below is recommended if the plating combination of fitting components is not known.

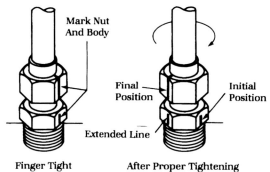

Finger Tight   After Proper Tightening

Assembly of Tube to 37° Flared Fitting Flat Method

Another means of assembly for 37° flare fittings is the flats from finger tight method or FFFT. This method requires that the tube and fitting are aligned and tightened by hand until some metal to metal contact causes a resistance to turning. The nut and body hex should be marked for an initial position.

Tighten the nut further until it rotates through the number of flats. If desired you may also mark the final position for later remakes or to given an indication of proper initial assembly.

Subsequent remakes will require less turns to produce a positive seal.

Flats from Finger Tight (FFFT) Table

The Flats From Finger Tight (FFFT) method requires turning the nut a specific number of flats. Shown is a representative table which gives the number of flats required at initial assembly.

The size of the fitting is found in the code, example: -4 fitting is a ¼" fitting, a -32 is a 2" fitting. Sizes incremented in 16ths.

Torque and FFFT Methods Compared

A comparison of the torque vs. flats method describes the advantages and disadvantages of the two methods. The torque method is fast, but it is difficult to visually inspect for proper tightening. The FFFT method is slower but provides consistent preload and visual inspection is easy because of markings on the fitting.

Size	Steel (F.F.F.T.)	Stainless Steel (F.F.F.T.)
*2	2.25 ± .25	2.00 ± .25
*3	2.25 ± .25	2.00 ± .25
4	2.25 ± .25	2.00 ± .25
*5	2.25 ± .25	2.00 ± .25
6	2.25 ± .25	2.25 ± .25
8	2.25 ± .25	2.25 ± .25
10	2.00 ± .25	2.00 ± .25
12	2.00 ± .25	1.50 ± .25
*14	2.00 ± .25	2.00 ± .25
16	2.00 ± .25	2.00 ± .25
20	2.00 ± .25	2.00 ± .25
24	2.00 ± .25	2.00 ± .25
32	2.00 ± .25	2.00 ± .25

*Estimate

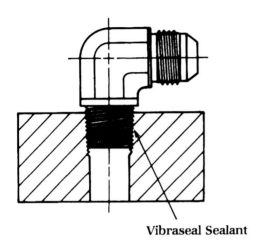

Vibraseal Sealant

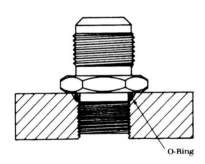

O-Ring

Assembly of Flareless Fitting

The flareless fittings require a minimum of instructions; you only need to align the tube and fitting, tighten the nut until finger tight, and turn an additional 1½ turns. It is important not to overtighten the nut or damage to the ferrule will occur.

On sizes larger than -8 (1/2" OD tube), it is desirable to preset the bite sleeve on a presetting machine prior to final assembly in the fitting.

Assembly of Face Seal Fitting

Assembly of the face seal fitting is also easy. Once aligned you need only to tighten the nut to the proper torque listed in the table.

Assembly of Pipe Thread Fitting to Port

Port fittings come in two basic varieties, pipe thread ports and straight thread. To assemble pipe thread ports, first visually inspect both threads so they are both free from nicks, burrs, dirt, etc. Apply sealant and tighten the fitting to the number of turns from finger tight as shown in the table. A high quality thread sealant will also retain the fitting and is usually more effective than Teflon tape or pipe dope.

Assembly of Straight Thread Fitting to Port

A more effective seal can be achieved by using SAE or ISO (metric) straight thread o-ring fittings. One such type of fitting is the nonadjustable variety. This fitting is quite easy to assemble. First inspect the threads, then lubricate the o-ring with a light coating of oil or compatible fluid and tighten to the torque level recommended by the manufacturer, or shown in the table.

Assembly of Adjustable Straight Thread Fitting

The assembly of adjustable straight thread o-ring fittings involves slightly more care than the nonadjustable variety. There are six steps that must be followed for proper assembly of adjustable straight thread o-ring fittings:

Step 1   Inspect and correct both mating parts for burrs, nicks, scratches or any foreign particles.
Step 2   Lubricate o-ring with light coat of oil or compatible fluid.
Step 3   Back off the lock nut as far as possible.
Step 4   Screw the fitting into the port by hand until the backup washer contacts the face of the port.
Step 5   Turn the position of the fitting to the desired position — but not more than one full turn.
Step 6   Hold the fitting in the desired position and tighten the lock nut to the torque level listed in table for nonadjustable straight thread o-ring fittings.

Pinched O-rings

Care should be taken to assure that all steps have been properly performed. Improper assembly can pinch the o-ring causing a leaky joint.

Assembly of 4-bolt Split Flange Fitting to Port

Illustrated is the final assembly of a 4-bolt split flange. Note the seal between the port and flange at the o-ring.

When assembling 4-bolt split flanges, care must be taken to insure that both surfaces are clean and free of burrs or nicks so as to not damage the o-ring during assembly.

Position the flanges as shown in the diagram and hand tighten all four bolts.

Tighten the bolts in a diagonal sequence and in small increments to the torque level recommended in the following table.

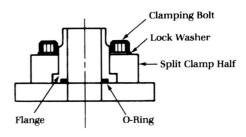

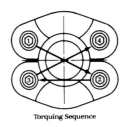

Torquing Sequence

4-Bolt Split Flange Torque Table

Flange Size	Code 61		Code 62	
	Bolt Thread	Torque (lb.-in.)	Bolt Thread	Torque (lb.-in.)
1/2	5/16-18	175-225	5/16-18	175-225
3/4	3/8-16	250-350	3/8-16	300-400
1	3/8-16	325-425	7/16-14	500-600
1 1/4	7/16-14	425-550	1/2-13	750-900
1 1/2	1/2-13	550-700	5/8-11	1400-1600
2	1/2-13	650-800	3/4-10	2400-2600

4-bolt Split Flange Torque Table

SAE Code 61 is for split flanges used in hydraulic systems with working pressure to 3000 psi (up to 5000 for smaller sizes) and Code 62 is for systems to 6000 psi.

Troubleshooting Fitting Failures

The procedure for troubleshooting various types of fitting assembly installations for leakage is to start with, determining where the leak location is; then checking the joints for proper tightness; and finally, if the joints continue to leak, to check for correct assembly and possible remake of the joint.

Abuse Failures

Leakage in a hydraulic system can often be traced to abuse. Tube and fitting damage can be caused by any of the following:

- Handling and storage. Threads and sealing surfaces can be damaged through rough handling. **DO NOT** remove the protective caps and plugs while putting parts in storage.
- Overtorquing - Thinking that "if a fitting leaks, tighten it a little more" is not always correct. Overtightening, more often than not, distorts parts and causes leakage.
- Using tube lines as structural supports, ladder rails, etc. This puts excessive strain on joints, causing leakage.

Problem	Probable Cause	Possible Remedy
Tube to fitting joint - leakage at 37 degree flare	A. Flare 45 degrees instead of 37 degrees	1. Replace and/or reflare.
	B. Flare has embedded burrs, dirt, grit, etc.	1. Replace and reflare tube.
	C. Severe scratches or indented weld seam.	1. Replace and reflare tube.
	D. Flare has crack	1. Replace tube.
	E. There is not a 360 degree line of contact on fitting nose	1. Replace and/or reflare tube.
	F. Tube is not properly aligned with fitting.	1. Rebend tube for proper alignment.
	G. Nose of fitting has nicks, scratches, chatter marks or other imperfections	1. Replace fitting.
	H. Nose of fitting is severely deformed (fitting too soft or overtightened)	1. Replace fitting. 2. Tighten to proper specification using either torque of FFFT method.
	I. Fitting seat is not concentric with threads	1. Replace fitting.
Port to fitting joint - leakage at pipe port	A. There is no sealant used or sealant was worn them	1. Remove fitting. 2. Apply new sealant and retighten to specification.
	B. Threads are galled	1. Replace fitting.
	C. Fitting screwed in too far in the port (port opened up or boss cracked)	1. Replace components.
	D. Threads are severely nicked	1. Replace fitting.
	E. Fitting loosens when system reaches operating temperature	1. Tighten fitting while at operating temperature. (NOT recommended if port is in a cast housing.)
	F. Seals initially but vibrates loose after some time	1. Replace with SAE straight thread port.

Problem	Probable Cause	Possible Remedy
Port to fitting joint - leakage at SAE straight thread o-ring port	A. Washer is too loose on adjustable fitting. (Washer should not move by its own weight or rock too much on the undercut.)	1. Replace fitting.
	B. Fitting threads are distorted (yielded)	1. Replace fitting.
	C. There are severe scratches or nicks on port face.	1. Reface the port. 2. Replace fittings and components.
	D. Spot face of port is smaller than washer diameter	1. Reface the port or replace the component.
	E. Port boss is cracked	1. Replace component.
	F. Port threads are distorted (yielded)	1. Replace component.
Port to fitting joint - leakage at 4-bolt split flange port	A. O-ring leaks	1. Replace with a good quality o-ring.
	B. Loose flange bolts.	1. Retighten flange bolts to specified torque following torquing procedure.
	C. Port has severe scratches or nicks in the seal area.	1. Resurface the port.
	D. Flace of the outer lip of flange has deep scratches and nicks.	1. Replace flange.
	E. Flange is distorted (overpressurized)	1. Replace flange. 2. Check system pressure. 3. Check compatibility of flange to system pressure.
	F. Clamp halves are distorted	1. Replace clamp halves. 2. Retorque using proper procedure and torque.
	G. Mounting bolts are bent	1. Check for signs of abuse. 2. Replace bolts using SAE Grade 5 or better.

Recommendations for
Leak Free Systems

In order to achieve a leak free hydraulic system follow these recommendations:

1. Think zero leakage from the very start — design for zero leakage.
2. Design in provisions for tube length variations and component movement due to hydraulic loads or changes in temperature.
3. Use proper clamping to dampen vibrations.
4. Use SAE or ISO straight thread ports for sizes one inch (or M33X2) and under; and four bolt flanges for larger sizes.
5. Specify the most cost effective fitting that meets your requirements best.
6. Specify SAE or ISO standard tubes, tube fittings, hose adapters and hose ends. Add performance requirements where missing.
7. Insist on U.S. or ISO standard connections on all equipment, domestic and foreign.
8. Insist on quality components. Buy from reputed suppliers that can provide necessary technical support including training.
9. Avoid indiscriminate mixing of components from different suppliers.
10. Train assembly personnel on a regular basis.
11. Use cylinder mounts that take thrust on their centerline.
12. Allow for component changes due to external force, pressure and/or temperature changes.
13. Remember that a well designed system put together with quality components by properly trained personnel using proper tools and procedures is the least costly system in the long run.

FLUIDS AND FILTER MAINTENANCE

The most common hydraulic fluid used in today's system is petroleum based hydraulic fluid. All fluids serve four basic functions in the system regardless of their chemical make-up:

1. To act as a medium for energy transmission.

2. To lubricate the general moving parts of the hydraulic components.

3. To act as a coolant for the system.

4. To seal the clearance between the close fitting and moving parts.

Petroleum fluid manufacturers will all try to improve their fluids by adding additives. Not all of these additives are found in every fluid, but where it is cost effective and plausible to use the additive packages, it is done.

Petroleum-Base Fluid Additives

Additive	Description
Antiwear (AW), Wear Resistant (WR) or Extreme Pressure (EP)	When added to the fluid, these agents reduce the rate of wear between parts. All three types of additives are not found in the same fluid and are not used in the same fluid application.
Antirust	This additive prevents the formation of rust on ferrous metals of the hydraulic system.
Antioxidant	Added to prevent fluid oxidation caused by the chemical reaction of petroleum fluid, water, oxygen, and metals in the hydraulic system.
Metal Deactivators	Prevents the catalytic effect of metals on the oxidation process of the fluid.
Foam Retardant	Used to inhibit the formation of foam in the reservoir.
Anticorrosives	Primarily added to fluids that will be used in the lubrication of bearings.
Viscosity Index (VI) Improvers	Used in fluids exposed to temperature extremes. VI improvers lower the rate of change of viscosity with changes in temperature.
Detergents	Helps to clean metal surfaces.
Demulsifiers	Unless your fluid is specifically designed to emulsify with water; this additive separates the water and petroleum fluid in the reservoir.
Vapor-phase Inhibitors	Generally found in ethylene glycol hydraulic fluids. Some petroleum fluids use them to inhibit rust formation especially in unprotected areas of the reservoir.
Pour Point Depressors	Used in fluids that are subjected to very low temperatures. The depressor lowers the natural pour point of the fluid.
Dispersants	Keeps solid contaminants suspended in the fluid preventing them from forming sludge.
Dye	Added by some manufacturers to aid in distinguishing their fluid and also in the detection of leaks.

Oil Problems

These additives are added to the fluid to minimize, correct or prevent some of the various oil problems such as high pressure lubrication, oil oxidation and oil contamination from water, air bubbles and dirt.

High Pressure Lubrication

As pressure climbs in a hydraulic system, the hydrodynamic fluid wedge (oil film) between moving parts has a tendency to break down. This breakdown allows for more friction and thus heat to be generated in the system.

There are three types of lubricity agents that can be added, each is used for different pressure ranges. For pressures below 1000 psi, Antiwear (AW) agents are used; for pressures between 1000 and 3000 psi, Wear Resistant (WR) agents are added to the fluid; and, for pressure above 3000 psi, Extreme Pressure (EP) additives are used.

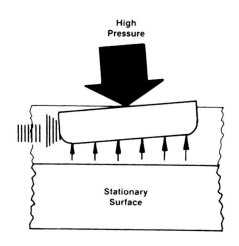

Check for High Pressure Lubrication

To check for a fluid's ability to give high pressure lubrication, check the manufacturer's catalog sheet. For example, with Gulf Oil's fluid titled "Harmony 48AW," the AW stands for antiwear. Or, with Sun Oil's fluid titled "Sunvis 816WR," the WR indicates wear resistant.

Many refiners do not indicate the antiwear additive in an oil title. Consequently, the refiner's catalog or data sheet for a particular fluid must be referred to.

Oil Oxidation

Oxidation of hydraulic fluid can be pinned down to basically two system locations: reservoir and pump outlet. In both cases, oil reacts with oxygen, but in different ways; and the oxidation products are not the same.

In a reservoir, the free surface of the oil reacts with oxygen in the air and water vapor. The product of this reaction includes weak acids and soaps. Acids weaken and pit component surfaces; soaps coat surfaces and can plug pressure-sensing orifices and lubrication paths.

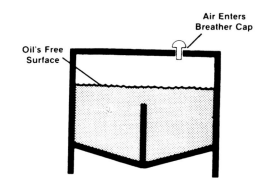

Besides the reservoir, another location where oil oxidation occurs is at the pump outlet. If air bubbles are present in a pump suction line as a result of an air leak or returning fluid velocity churning up the reservoir, they are compressed when exposed to high pressure and explode generating high temperature. The high temperature fries the oil, forming resinous products and causes the oil to acquire a characteristic burnt odor.

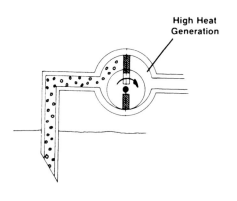

Resinous material forms a varnish or lacquer coating on the surfaces of components causing parts to stick. Also, sludge is formed by this resinous material which combines with dirt and floats around the system plugging small openings in valves and filters, and interferes with heat transfer to reservoir walls.

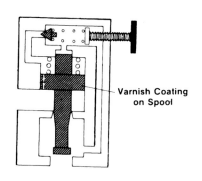

Check for Oxidized Oil

A check for oxidized oil is performed by comparing a sample of the questionable fluid with a sample of new fluid out of a drum. With both fluid samples at the same temperature, the new fluid will tend to stick to your fingers as it is poured over your hand.

Oxidized fluid feels very much like water. As it is poured over your hand and fingers, oxidized fluid runs off just as water. Also, fluid that has oxidized due to the high temperature created by exploding air bubbles will have a characteristic pungent odor.

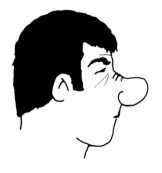

These are quick field checks, but to accurately check the condition of the questionable fluid, a sample should be sent to a lab for analysis. If this is impractical, the system should be drained, flushed and refilled with filtered fluid.

Water in Hydraulic Oil

All hydraulic oils contain water in varying degrees. This can be the result of condensation in a system reservoir, or direct contamination due to poor housekeeping practices, or coolant dripping on retracting piston rods. Any appreciable amount (greater than .5% by volume) will promote rusting, reduce lubrication and act as a catalyst to speed up the oxidation process of the oil, thereby increasing the problem of corrosion.

The process of corrosion dissolves metal and washes it away, reducing the metal part size and weight. On the other hand, rusting adds materials to a ferrous surface, increasing its size and weight.

Check for Water in Hydraulic Oil

A check for water in hydraulic oil which does not contain a color dye is performed by comparing a sample of the questionable fluid with a sample of new fluid. By pouring the samples into beakers or glass jars, hold them up to a light. You will notice that the new fluid looks crystal; it sparkles a little.

If the questionable fluid contains .5% water, it will appear dull or smokey. If it contains 1% or more water, it will look milky. (NOTE: Samples of new oil may be contaminated with water.)

An additional means of checking for water in an oil is to heat a fluid sample which appears smokey or milky. If the sample clears after a time, the oil probably contained water.

Foaming

In some systems where leaks are prevalent and/or returning oil is churned up as it enters a reservoir, foaming of the oil occurs. As a result, entrained air is

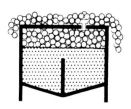

pumped into the system, causing spongy, erratic operation, rapid oil oxidation and noise. In more severe cases, oil foam could bubble out of the reservoir creating a housekeeping problem.

Check for Foaming

A check for foaming oil is performed by taking a fluid sample. The sample should be taken by removing the filler/breather cap and screen. Insert a glass or plastic tube (thief) about 2 feet (609.6 mm) in length and draw up a sample by placing a finger over the open top end of the thief or by a syringe bulb on the top end of thief. The sample should be taken as close to the pump inlet as possible with the machine running. Place the fluid sample into a bottle and inspect the sample for air bubbles.

Another indication that air bubbles are present in a system is noise. As air bubbles are drawn into the pump inlet, the pump will emit loud popping, banging and erratic noises.

An additional indication of air bubbles is spongy sytem operation. This is evidenced by erratic actuator movements and erratic gage reading as a system is operating.

Thief

Dirt in Oil

Dirt in a hydraulic system can be built into a system during manufacturing, handling and assembling of components and systems. Dirt can be generated in a system as a result of internal moving parts, flexing of component housings and rust. Dirt can also be added to a system as a result of servicing failed system components, not servicing reservoirs and cylinder rods pulling dirt in as they retract.

Check for Dirt in Oil

To check for iron-bearing metal particles, the reservoir filler/breather cap and screen can be removed, a small magnet

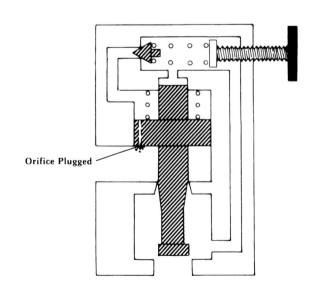

Orifice Plugged

attached to a rod can be inserted. With magnet submerged below fluid, operate the system at normal perating temperature; after a period withdraw magnet and inspect.

Trying to determine the dirt level of a fluid with the unaided eye can be virtually impossible because of the micro-fine particles of dirt that may be present. For a quick qualitative check on the fluid cleanliness level, use a portable fluid analysis kit. However, lab analysis on the fluid is your most accurate way to classify the cleanliness level of the questionable fluid.

Fire Resistant Hydraulic Fluid

In some systems or applications petroleum oil has a major disadvantage -- it has been the source of many industrial fires. In fire hazardous industrial environments where undisturbed production and operator safety are of primary concern, fire resistant fluids are employed.

Hydraulic fluids which are classified as fire resistant have:

Higher flash points - the temperature to which a fluid must be heated to give off sufficient vapor to ignite when a flame is applied. This temperature is well above 450°F (232°C).

Higher fire points - the temperature to which a fluid must be heated to burn continuously after a flame has been removed.

Higher spontaneous ignition temperature - the temperature at which a fluid ignites, without an external flame or spark. This temperature is above 700°F (371°C).

Water Base Fluid

A water base hydraulic fluid made up of water emulsified with 1-10% oil, is an oil-in-water emulsion commonly referred to as soluble oil fluid or high water content fluid (H.W.C.F.). This fluid is relatively inexpensive because the percentage of water is at least 90%.

But, this does lower the fluid's lubrication quality thus reducing component life. Another emulsion is a water-in-oil mixture where 60% is oil and 40% is water. Commonly called an invert emulsion, it has an increased lubricating characteristic with a slight decrease in fire resistance when compared to the oil-in-water emulsion.

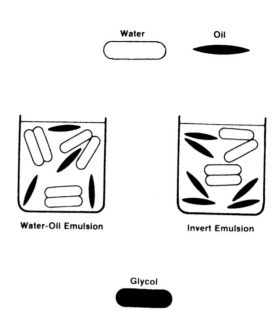

Water-Oil Emulsion   Invert Emulsion

Water glycol is another type of water base fire resistant fluid. It consists of water and a glycol which has a chemical structure very similar to automotive antifreeze. Water glycol is many times dyed red or pink, and normally consists of 60% glycol and 40% water, along with a chemical thickener to increase its viscosity. The glycol actually mixes with the water, thus being homogenous and not two-phase like emulsions. In addition, water glycol fluids are designed to work well at low temperatures.

Water Glycol

Problems with Water Base Fluid

With a water base fire resistant fluid in a system's reservoir, problems other than those discussed with petroleum oil can arise. Four specified problems related to water case fluids are: phase separation, bacteria formation, water evaporation and cavitation.

Phase Separation

Water base fluids are not designed to be operated at low temperatures. At 32°F, ice crystals begin to form. As the system operates and the temperature increases, the ice crystals melt but do not necessarily emulsify again. Repeated freezing and thawing could cause water and oil phases to separate to a large degree. As a result, fire resistance and lubricity are affected.

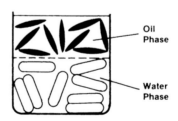

Oil Phase

Water Phase

Check for Phase Separation

A check for phase separation is performed by inspection. Drain off a fluid sample, while the machine is running, into a jar and allow the fluid to rest for a period of time; you will notice that any free water will settle to the bottom in the case of an invert emulsion and in an oil-in-water emulsion, oil would rise to the top. This indicates a problem within the system such as too much water being created due to condensation; freezing and thawing of fluid; or improperly mixed fluids, etc.

Bacteria Formation

In some situations, under the proper temperature conditions, a water base fluid can support the growth of bacteria. Bacteria in large quantities can plug pressure control valves and pressure compensated flow controls. Bacteria can also plug filter elements. Many water base fluid manufacturers place a bacteriacide additive in their fluid to combat this growth.

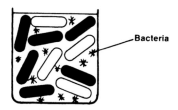

Check for Bacteria Formation

A check for bacteria formation is performed by sight and smell. If bacteria is present, inlet filters will appear to be coated by mucous or slime. And, the bacteria will give off a very offensive odor.

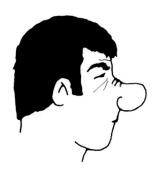

Water Evaporation

Many fluid manufacturers recommend that oil-in-water emulsions operate in a system at temperatures between 32°F to 122°F (0°C to 50°C) and these fluids are not recommended for high bearing load systems. Water-in-oil emulsions have a temperature operating range of 16°F to 151°F (-9°C to 66°C). Water-glycol fluids should be operated at temperatures below 122°F (50°C) to avoid water evaporation, vapor phase inhibitor depletion and an increase in viscosity.

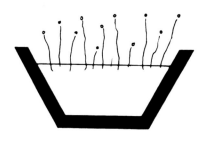

As water evaporates, the water vapor that forms can condense on unprotected ferrous parts causing rust. The fluid's fire resistance quality decreases because of the direct relationship between the percentage of water and fluid's resistance to burning. Fluid viscosity is also affected. In an emulsion the viscosity decreases or even becomes unstable and in a water-glycol the viscosity increases.)

To insure proper water content of the various water base fire resistant fluids, monitoring of the fluid should be done by lab analysis on a regular interval.

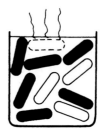

Water Evaporation

Synthetic Fire Resistant Fluid

Synthetic fire resistant fluids are man-made liquids which are praised for their resistance to burning while performing close to petroleum oil with respect to lubrication. Common types of synthetic fire resistant fluids are phosphate ester and synthesized hydrocarbon base.

Problems Related to all Fire Resistant Fluids

We discussed earlier problems that are specifically related to water base fire resistant fluid. But, there are some problems that result from the use of any type of fire resistant fluid. Some of these problems are compatibility with seals and protective coatings, foam and air retention, and dirt retention.

Compatibility Problem

The common Buna N seal material used for dynamic sealing of a petroleum base fluid is also compatible with emulsions, water glycol and synthesized hydrocarbon base fluids. However, this seal is not acceptable for a phosphate ester or phosphate ester blend fluid. These fluids require Viton, or any other suitable material.

If a reservoir interior has a protective coating compatible with petroleum base fluid, the use of water base and synthetic fluids tend to dissolve these coatings. The coating then becomes trapped by the suction strainer and/or suction filter creating a high restriction at the pump inlet resulting in pump cavitation.

Most of your common metals used in the construction of hydraulic components are not compatible with emulsions and synthetic fluids. They attack such metals as zinc, cadmium, magnesium, lead and certain aluminum alloys. Examples of such components might be galvanized pipe, and zinc or cadmium plated strainers, fittings and reservoir accessories. Most high water content fluids will not attack bronze and anodized aluminum.

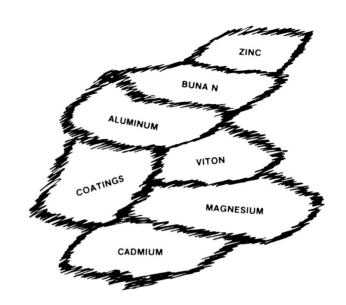

Foaming and Air Retention

Water base and synthetic fluids have more of a tendency to retain air and to foam compared to petroleum base fluids. After returning to the reservoir, fire resistant fluids require more time in a reservoir to give up any accumulated air bubbles. Consequently, systems using fire resistant fluid should have larger reservoirs than comparable systems using petroleum fluid, or some other method to release the entrained air.

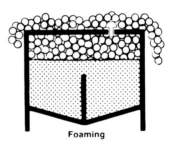

Foaming

Dirt Retention

As fire resistant fluid returns to the reservoir, it has more of a tendency to retain dirt particles in suspension compared to petroleum fluid. When a fire resistant fluid is used, good filtration should be a prime consideration. And, the use of magnets should not be overlooked to remove ferrous metal particles that are suspended in the fluid inside the reservoir.

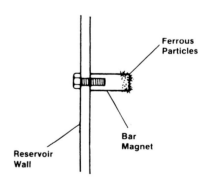

Fluid Maintenance Considerations

Maintenance considerations of fire resistant fluids and petroleum base fluids with regard to storage are basically the same. That is, store barrels on their sides when out of doors and under shelter so that water does not leak into the fluid. Additionally, with emulsion fluids, care should be taken to store these fluids in an area where they are not exposed to low temperatures. Constant freezing and thawing will affect their stability, they may develop phase separation.

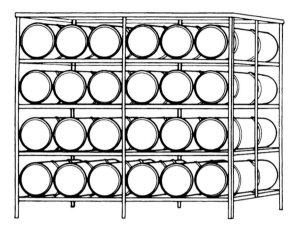

Transferring oil from barrel to reservoir is another important consideration. Before the drum plugs are removed, the drum cover should be cleaned. This procedure should also be followed for any apparatus or tools which will be used in the process such as hoses, pumps, funnels, reservoir filler holes and the operator's hands. A check should be made to see that the barrel contains the correct fluid by brand name and viscosity. And, if a pump is used to transfer the fluid, care should be taken that the pump is not filled with a different fluid and that pump materials and transfer assemblies (hose fittings, etc.) are compatible with the fluid.

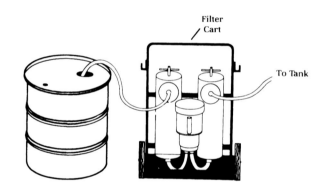

Filter Cart

To Tank

The fluid that is in the reservoir should be maintained and monitored at regular intervals. Maintenance of the fluid includes filling a reservoir when its minimum oil level has been reached, fixing leaks and servicing filters. In addition, a fluid sample should be taken for analysis on a regular basis.

Adding water to an emulsion fluid is not normally recommended because of the critical mixing process which is demanded. Adding water to a water glycol solution is common, but it is not a simple matter of running a hose to the reservoir from the nearest water tap. Make-up water should be free of mineral deposits which could contaminate a system. Distilled steam condensate or deionized water are suitable for use in a water-glycol solution. The amount of water to be added is determined after analysis of the fluid sample by a lab.

Maintaining Proper Fluid Temperature

Hot fluid in your equipment's hydraulic system is one of the primary causes of poor operation, component failure and downtime. Here are some pointers on maintaining proper fluid temperature.

The fluid in your hydraulic system was designed for operation within a specific temperature range. You may be able to run it at hotter temperatures for short periods of time, intermittently, without adverse effects. If you run continuously with fluid that is too hot, however, your equipment will operate poorly and eventually key components will fail and halt your machine.

How Hot is "Too Hot"

"Hot fluid" is a relative term. 120°F (49°C) at the reservoir is considered an ideal operating temperature for petroleum based fluid. Hydraulic systems that are designed to operate with high water content fluids have a lower temperature range. Some synthetic fluids such as synthesized hydrocarbons have maximum operating temperature ranges of 250°F (212°C). Always take fluid temperature reading at the reservoir, not at a component or any of the piping.

Measuring Fluid Temperature

There are several ways to check the temperature of the fluid. The most accurate method is by means of a thermometer. On some machines, this is mounted on the reservoir. Make it a habit to check the thermometer frequently, while the equipment is running.

If the machine doesn't have a reservoir thermometer, use the "palm test." First check the tank with your fingertip; if it's not too hot to touch, place your palm on the tank. You'll be able to hold it there without discomfort if the fluid temperature is about 130°F (54°C) or below.

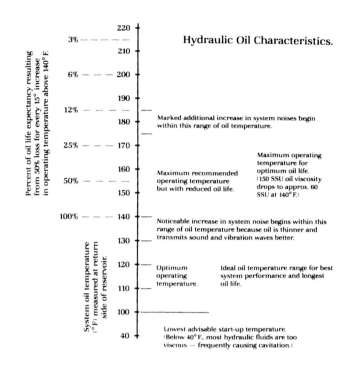

Hydraulic Oil Characteristics.

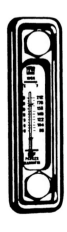

Isolating Trouble Spots

To determine which components are "running hot" and overheating the fluid, feel the outlet fittings and lines at the valves, pumps and motors. If the fluid is normal going into a component but hot coming out, that could be one of the troublemakers.

CAUTION: Be very careful when performing the touch test. Severe burns can occur.

A sticking valve can cause excessive heat. If a spool does not return promptly to the neutral position, the pump flow will be dumped continuously. This builds up heat rapidly.

If a relief valve is set too low, part of the fluid will be dumped across the valve with every cycle. This too generates excessive heat. Even when all valves are set properly, they may not be operating well because of worn orifices, excessive clearances or seals.

The chart shows representative examples of heat generation at various components in a hydraulic system operating under given conditions.

SYSTEM COMPONENT	CAUSE OF HEAT	PRESSURE DROP	HEAT LOSS* (BTU/HR)
11 gpm pump @ 1000 psi	Pressure drop and surface tension during slippage back to pump inlet or to reservoir through drain.	1000 psi (.8 gpm)	1200
½" pipe or hose @ 10 gpm	Normal line pressure drop and surface tension at walls	.55 psi/ft.	7.25/ft.
½"-90° El pipe @ 10 gpm	Pressure drop plus friction at sharp turn in flow path.	.94 psi	14.1/El
½" 4-way spool-type directional control valve @ 10 gpm and 1000 psi	Leakage friction across both lands.	.86 psi	13
	Pressure drop plus friction at turns and orifices.	41 psi	615
½" angle check valve @ 20 gpm	Pressure drop plus restricted passage of fluid through valve while providing back pressure for shifting piloted valves.	65 psi (Spring tension)	190
Relief valve (on press) @ 10 gpm	Pressure drop plus restricted passage of relief fluid through valve during feed, dwell and reload cycles.	1000 psi	10,500

*For oil of 150 SSU viscosity.

Preventive Measures

How can you keep your equipment's hydraulic system from running too hot?

1. Set up a regular schedule for checking the fluid temperature, appearance, smell, feel and contamination analysis. Change fluid as recommended by the equipment manufacturer.

2. Be prompt about removing, checking and repairing or replacing valves, pumps, or other components that are running hot.

3. If relief or flow control valves are running hot, check and adjust their settings. Check also for proper sizing of components and for overload conditions.

4. Break in new components gradually. New, close-fitting parts expand at different rates, and are especially prone to seizure when they get too hot.

5. To start a newly installed pump or motor with hot fluid in the reservoir, jog the pump or motor just enough to draw the hot fluid into the component. Then wait a few minutes to allow the temperature to equalize in all the component parts. Repeat until the temperature on the outside of the pump or motor is the same as that on the piping.

6. Keep your equipment clean. A thick layer of dirt acts as insulation. It will prevent the hydraulic system from getting rid of heat.

7. On hot days, and in hot climates, keep a constant check on fluid temperature. Be sure to use a fluid recommended for hot weather operation by the equipment manufacturer or fluid supplier.

8. If excessive heat persists, the use of a cooling system should be investigated.

Troubleshooting

Troubleshooting hydraulic fluid is done by sight, feel, smell and analysis. The following charts will present some of the more common fluid problems.

Problem	Probable Cause
Dirty fluid	A. Components not properly cleaned after servicing. B. Inadequate screening in fill pipe. (Too large a mesh) C. Tank air breather removed. (No breather provided.) D. Open end of pipe lines and/or hoses not properly covered while servicing machine. E. Improper tank baffles not providing settling basin for heavy materials. F. Inadequate filtration or bypassing filter. G. Unclean fluid being added to the reservoir. H. Excessive component wear.
Foaming fluid	A. Fluid return line not below fluid level. B. Inadequate or broken baffles in reservoir. C. Leak at suction side of pump. D. Lack of anti-foaming additive. E. Excessive flow to tank through tank return line. F. Too high a velocity flow through tank return line. G. Bad pump shaft seal.
Excessive water in petroleum base fluid	A. Tank cooling coils not below fluid level. B. Cold water lines fastened directly against hot tank causing condensation within tank. C. Filler pipe left open. D. Water in cans used to replace fluid in tank. E. Extreme temperature differential in certain geographical locations. F. Drain not provided at lowest point in tank to remove water collected over possible long operating periods.

Overheating of system fluid	A. Water shutoff or heat exchanger clogged.
	B. Continuous flow over relief valve.
	   1. Stalling under load, etc.
	   2. Fluid viscosity too high or low.
	C. Excessive slippage or internal leakage at pump or valve(s).
	D. Reservoir size too small.
	E. Reservoir assembled without baffling or sufficient baffling.
	F. Case drain line from pump returning oil too close to suction line.
	G. Pipe, tube or hose I.D. too small causing high turbulence.
	H. Valving too small, causing high turbulence.
	I. Poor air circulation around reservoir.
	J. System relief valve set too high.

Fluid Sampling Procedures

When a maintenance schedule is put together for the servicing of your equipment, the drawing of a fluid sample should be included in the schedule. Analysis of this sample can be your most accurate method of pinpointing impending failure in your equipment.

Drawing a fluid sample involves many steps to make sure you are getting a representative sample. Often erroneous sampling procedures will disguise the true nature of system cleanliness levels. For best results, use one of the following methods to obtain a representative system fluid sample.

For Systems with a Sampling Valve

1. Operate system until the operating temperature has stabilized.

2. With the system operating, open the sample valve allowing 7 to 16 ounces (200 to 500 ml) of fluid to flush the sampling port. The sampling valve design should provide turbulent flow through the sampling port.

3. Using a wide mouth, pre-cleaned sampling bottle (per ANSI/B93.20-1972 specification) remove the bottle cap and place in the stream of flow from the sampling valve. DO NOT "rinse" out the bottle with the initial sample. Do not set the bottle cap on dirty, contaminated surfaces. Fill the bottle within no more than one inch of the top.

4. Close the sample bottle immediately. Next, close the sampling valve. (Make prior provisions to "catch" the fluid while removing the bottle from the stream.)

5. Tag the sample bottle with pertinent data: include date, machine number, fluid supplier, fluid number code, fluid type and time elapsed since last sample (if any).

Systems without a Sampling Valve

There are two locations to obtain a sample in a system without a sampling valve: in-tank and in the line. The procedure for both follows.

In the Tank Sampling

1. Operate the system until the operating temperature has stabilized.

2. Use a small hand held vacuum pump bottle thief or syringe with tubing to extract sample. Insert sampling device into the tank to one half the fluid height. You will probably have to weight the end of the sampling tube. Your objective is to obtain a sample in the middle portion of the tank. Avoid the top or bottom of the tank. Do not let the syringe or tubing come in contact with the side or bottom of the tank.

3. Put extracted fluid into an approved, pre-cleaned sample bottle as described in the sampling valve method.

4. Cap immediately.

5. Tag with information as described in sampling valve method.

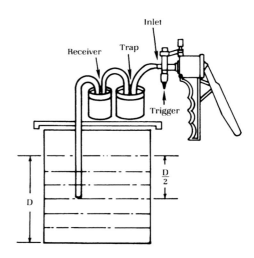

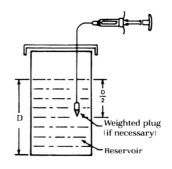

In-line Sampling

1. Operate the system until the operating temperature has stabilized.

2. Locate a suitable valve in the system where turbulent flow can be obtained (ball valve is preferred). If no such valve exists, locate a fitting which can be easily opened to provide turbulent flow (tee or elbow).

3. Flush the valve or fitting sample point with a highly filtered solvent such as freon. Open valve or fitting and allow fluid to flush out the valve or fitting. (Take care to allow for this step. Direct sample back to tank or into large

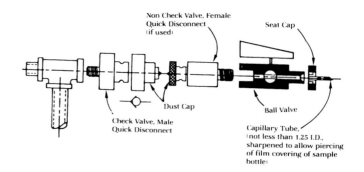

container. It is not necessary to discard this fluid.)

4. Place an approved and pre-cleaned sample bottle under the stream of flow per sampling valve method.

5. Cap sample bottle immediately.

6. Tag with important information per the sampling valve method.

SAFETY NOTE: Select a valve or fitting where the pressure is limited to 200 psig or less.

Regardless of method being used, observe common sense rules. Any equipment which is used in the fluid sampling procedure must be washed and rinsed with a highly filtered solvent. This includes a vacuum pump, syringe and tubing. Your goal is to count only the particles already in the system fluid. Dirty sampling devices and non-representative samples will lead to erroneous conclusions and cost you more in the long run.

These samples are analyzed in most laboratories for:

1. Viscosity - the resistance of a liquid flow. A change in viscosity may mean a decrease in machine performance because of increased leakage, higher pressure drops, lack of lubrication, and/or overheating. It may also mean that an incorrect fluid was used to fill the machine's reservoir. A change in viscosity ±10% from original specifications or from a previous sample is considered excessive.

2. Neutralization Number - a number which indicates the amount of potassium hydroxide needed to neutralize the acid in a fluid. A check on neutralization number is performed to determine if additives have deteriorated or oxidation is excessive.

3. Water Content - in hydraulic fluid it reduces lubrication and affects addi-

tives and promotes oxidation. Water content exceeding
.5% by volume is considered excessive.

4. Particle Count - the particles in a 100 ml fluid sample are counted and reported in particle size ranges. Particle counts indicate the overall effectiveness of the system filters. Most reports show both a graph (particle size vs. number of particles). At the very least, a cleanliness level should be assigned to describe the contamination content (e.g. ISO 4406 standard reporting).

5. Spectrographic Analysis - may be used to determine the presence of required additives, wear generated metals, and other contaminants. These results are reported in "ppm" and may indicate the sources of wear problems.

Significant changes in one or more of these analysis factors can signal changes in system operation or indicate the possiblity of a potential problem.

Filtration

The function of a filter is to remove the contamination in a hydraulic system. Filters are not put into the system just to keep the fluid clean, but rather to provide some overall economic benefits. A filter is used to guard against potential breakdown and damage due to dirt in the hydraulic system. We can safely say that most of all maintenance downtime and malfunctions are due to contamination.

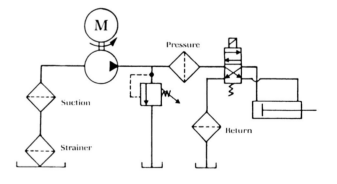

Types of Filter Media

There are a wide variety of filter medias that are used in industry today to remove contamination. They fall into two general categories:

Depth type media
Surface type media

Depth Filter Media

Whatever media is used such as paper, synthetic, composite or wire mesh, it is put into a filter housing. The fluid is forced to flow through an appreciable thickness of many layers of filter media. The dirt is trapped in the interwinding passages within the media, as well as on the media surface.

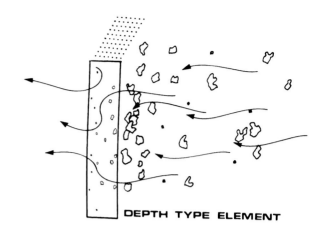

DEPTH TYPE ELEMENT

Surface Filter Media

Surface type elements are constructed of a single layer of filter material. Dirt is caught on the surface of the media. The most common type of surface filter media is woven fiber, such as woven wire cloth.

What Filter Media to Use

A question that often arises when installing a filter on a piece of equipment is "Which type do we use, surface type or depth type?" By looking at the system in which the filter will be installed, and by considering the advantages and disadvantages of each type, a proper selection can be made.

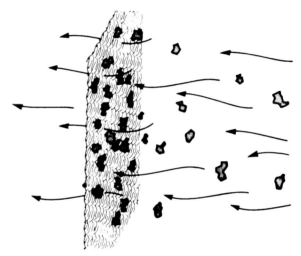

SURFACE TYPE ELEMENT

Depth Type Filter - Advantages and Disadvantages

Advantages:

- High dirt capacities
- Inexpensive
- High efficiency

Disadvantages:

- Impractical to clean
- Media migration possibilities
- Limited chemical compatibility
- Shelf life limitation
- Higher initial pressure differential

Surface Type Filter - Advantages and Disadvantages

Advantages:

- Freedom from media migration
- Resistant to fatigue, temperature and corrosion
- Cleanable
- Controlled pore size
- Low initial pressure differential

Disadvantages:

- Expensive
- Not initially efficient
- Limited dirt holding capacity

By considering these factors, the proper selection of media can be made.

Filter Installation

There are basically four different locations where filters can be installed. One is on the suction side of the pump; a second is on the pressure side of the pump; the third is in the return line; and the fourth is off-line.

Suction Filter and Strainer Characteristics

Suction filters and strainers are designed for low pressure drop conditions to prevent cavitation of the pump. When a suction filter is installed in the system, it displays these characteristics:

1. It directly protects the pump and the rest of the system from dirt introduced through the reservoir.

2. It minimizes catastrophic failure due to a single particle.

3. Since it operates with low fluid velocities and low differential pressure, filter efficiency is enhanced due to the formation of a "cake" on the element.

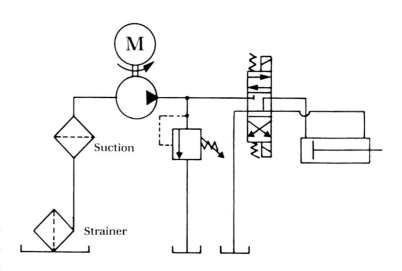

Suction Filter and Straining Considerations

Despite the pluses of a suction filter or strainer, if the pressure drop on the suction side of a pump (due to all pipes and restrictions including the suction filter) exceeds the pump manufacturer's maximum recommended suction specifications, cavitation will occur. Thus only low pressure drops across the filter media are permissable. If fine filtration is attempted on the suction line, a much larger housing is needed, and only limited filter life is available. It may not be suitable for many variable volume pumps; consult your pump manufacturer.

Pressure Filter Installation and Characteristics

Filters can be installed on the downstream or pressure side of a pump. Fluid leaving the pump would be forced through the pressure filter which has these characteristics:

1. Pressure filters can filter to very fine degrees, without as much concern for pressure differential.

2. Pressure filters can provide specific component protection.

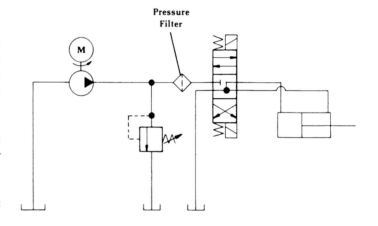

Pressure Filter

Pressure Filter Considerations

To prevent failures in the hydraulic system due to the installation of a pressure filter, note these considerations:

1. The housing of a pressure filter must be designed to handle the high pressure of the full system operation, including shock conditions, vibrations and transient responses, thus making it relatively expensive.

2. The advantage of cake filtration is lost with high differential pressure due to penetration of the filter media. The rapid change in pressure conditions within a pressure filter can damage the element if not specifically de-

signed for high differential pressures or surges in flow rate.

3. The element cannot catch debris from downstream components. Nor does it catch particles entering the system through worn cylinder rod seals and other working components.

Return Line Filter Installation and Characteristics

A filter can be installed in the return line or return line header pipe. The filter should be the last thing the fluid encounters before returning to the reservoir. The characteristics of this filter installation are:

1. It protects the reservoir from dirt that is generated within the system; therefore, removing it before it is again passed through the system.

2. Since the return filter is exposed to only differential pressures, the housing is designed more economically.

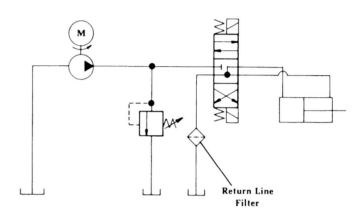

Return Line Filter

Return Line Filter Considerations

To minimize system problems due to the installation of a return line filter, note these considerations:

1. There is no direct protection for components from contamination introduced from the reservoir.

2. Return line flow surges from discharging actuators, accumulators and other operating components must be considered when sizing a return line filter.

3. Flow surges affect the caking effect on the element and make it less efficient.

4. Backpressures generated by the differential pressure across the filter can affect the operation of system components.

Off-line or Side Stream Filter Installation

Off-line or side stream filtration consists of a pump, filter and the appropriate connections. These components are installed off-line as a small subsystem, separate from the working lines, or included in a fluid cooling loop. Fluid is pumped out of the reservoir, through the filter, and back to the reservoir, in a continuous fashion. By selecting the appropriate pump flow rate and filter efficiency, this type of filtration can keep the fluid as clean as is necessary for most systems. The characteristics of this filter installation are:

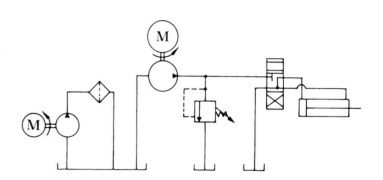

1. Servicing of the filter(s) is possible without loss of production.

2. A fixed flow rate from the pump eliminates surges, allowing for optimal element life and performance.

3. The ability to integrate cooling and filtering of the fluid is made easy with off-line or side stream filtering.

Off-line of Side Stream Filtering Considerations

To minimize system problems due to the installation of an off-line or side stream filter, note these considerations:

1. There is no direct component protection from contamination introduced into the system at any point.

2. The initial cost of installation is relatively high.

3. Space requirements for a subsystem of this type is often restrictive.

Filters must be Maintained

The key to good filtration is filter maintenance. A machine may be equipped with the best filters available and they may be positioned in the system where they do the most good; but, if the filters are not taken care of and cleaned when dirty, the money spent for the filters and their installation has been wasted. A filter can be no better than the maintenance afforded it.

Maintenance Suggestions

Good filter maintenance can be accomplished by the following these suggestions:

1. Set up a filter maintenance schedule and follow it diligently.

2. Inspect filter elements that have been removed from the system for signs of failure which may indicate that service interval should be shortened, and of impending systems problems.

Realistically, filter change seems to depend more on the conditions governing the operation of individual machines rather than on the time they are in operation. Filters which signal the condition of their filter elements by mechanical or electrical indicator would be far easier to maintain than servicing by the calendar time periods.

Troubleshooting Filters

Many times problems with the hydraulic system can be traced to the specific filtering system being used.

Problem	Probable Cause	Possible Remedy
Slow component operation	A. Restricted return return filter	1. Check for bypass of element. Replace element.
	B. Improper size element.	1. Replace element with proper size.
	C. Restricted suction filter	1. Check for high vaccum reading. 2. Replace or clean filter element.
	D. Restricted pressure	1. Check for high differential across filter. 2. Replace element.
Pump makes excessive noise	A. Restricted suction filter (cavitation)	1. Check for high inlet vacuum. 2. Replace or clean element.
	B. Loose filter housing cover (aeration)	1. Check for loose mounting bolts on cover. 2. Check for and replace worn cover gasket.
	C. Low fluid level (aeration)	1. Check fluid level in tank. Refill to proper level with clean fluid.
Fluid contains contamination	A. Improper type of filter element	1. Determine if the micron rating of element is correct for application. 2. Check for bypass condition.
	B. Plugged element	1. Replace or clean element.
	C. Filter change interval too long	1. Decrease time between filter change period. 2. Add bypass indicators to filters.
	D. Pressure differential too high	1. Check for high inlet pressure. 2. Replace element with a high pressure element and housing.
	E. Ruptured element	1. Check for stuck bypass; repair or replace. 2. Replace element. 3. Check for high pressure surging.
	F. No element	1. Install proper element
Bypass indicator always reads "Bypass"	A. Fluid viscosity too high.	1. Check for recommended fluid viscosity.
	B. Broken spring or weak spring	1. Remove and replace bypass spring.
	C. Plugged element	1. Replace or clean element.

Problem	Probable Cause	Possible Remedy
Bypass indicator reads "Filter is clean"	A. No element installed.	1. Install element
	B. Ruptured element	1. Replace element. 2. Refer to ruptured element problem.
	C. Broken spring	1. Remove and replace bypass spring.
Broken filter housing	A. Too high pressure	1. Check for pressure surges and correct. 2. Check suitability of housing for application.
	B. Shock pressures	1. Install shock suppressor (accumulator).
Ruptured element	A. Bypass not installed or stuck close	1. Check housing for installed bypass. 2. Check for broken spring or guide stem. Replace bypass.
	B. Too high pressure	1. Check suitability of element for application.
	C. Change interval too long	1. Decrease time bewteen filter change period. 2. Add bypass indicator to filter application.
Filter indicator reads "bypass" upon start up	A. Oil viscosity high during cold startup	1. Run system until it reaches normal operating temperature.
	B. Highly contaminated system (If new system has not been flushed, it's common to load a filter with dirt within minutes of initial startup initial startup	1. In new systems, flush with low viscosity fluid at high velocities. 2. Replace filter element several times until fluid is cleaned up. 3. In existing systems, consult specialist and replace filter element(s).
	C. Filter bypass setting too low relative to filter pressure drop with a clean element installed (for given conditions)	1. Select a higher bypass setting if available and if circuit conditions will permit. 2. Replace filter with a larger one with a lower pressure drop.
	D. Wrong element installed (filter media too fine and/or pressure drop too high	1. Replace wrong element with correct one.
	E. Filter indicator out of calibration	1. Check indicator, most will read "CLEAN" when system is shut down and there is no flow through filter. 2. Replace or calibrate indicator

Preventive Maintenance Points to Remember

1. Before start up of new equipment, clean out the entire hydraulic system. This gets rid of "factory dirt."

2. Make sure that all clean-out holes, filler caps and breather cap filters on the reservoir are properly fastened. Do not run the system unless all normally provided filtration devices are in place.

3. Make certain that the fluid used in the system is of a type recommended by the manufacturers of the system or components.

4. Keep the oil reservoir filled to the recommended level. This helps prevent formation of rust.

5. Always keep the supply of fresh fluid covered tightly. If you store hydraulic oil drums outdoors, store them on their sides, not standing upright.

6. Do not return to the system any fluid which has leaked out unless it has been finely filtered.

7. When repairing, cleaning or replacing components, use common sense precautions to prevent entry of dirt into components that have been temporarily removed from the circuit.

8. Before changing from one type of fluid to another, or after a major failure in the system, flush the hydraulic system.

9. Use clean containers, hoses and funnels when filling the reservoir. Use of a filter cart or a portable pump/filter transfer unit when adding fluid is highly recommended.

10. Watch filter elements and magnetic filter cores for metallic particles. They are signs of wear inside pumps, valves, etc., and cause rapid wear and eventual breakdown of other components.

11. Check component mountings for looseness and tighten down as needed. Vibrating components will shake rust and metallic particles into the fluid stream.

12. Draw fluid samples on a regular basis for analysis.

13. Follow the equipment manual recommendations for cleaning and changing hydraulic filter elements and the fluid itself.

Index